Letts
and
LONSDALE

GCSE
Success

Revision Guide

Science
Foundation

Brian Arnold • Hannah Kingston • Emma Poole

Contents

Physics

A balanced diet and nutrition

The seven nutrition groups are *carbohydrates, proteins, fat, vitamins and minerals, fibre and water.* A balanced diet is made up of all of the above nutrients.

Carbohydrates

Carbohydrates consist of starch and types of sugar, e.g. glucose (the sugar our bodies use for respiration) and lactose (the sugar in milk). We need carbohydrates to **give us energy**.

Starch is made up of smaller glucose molecules joined together, which means it has to be broken down first to give us energy. Starch is a slow release energy source, whereas glucose is more immediate.

The amount of energy a person needs in their diet depends on **age, gender and the amount of activity** they do. If a person takes in a larger

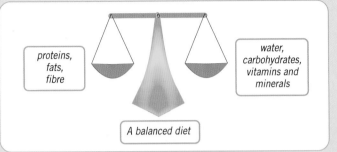

proteins, fats, fibre

water, carbohydrates, vitamins and minerals

A balanced diet

amount of energy than they use up exercising, the excess is stored as fat.

If a person becomes overweight, they are more likely to suffer health problems such as arthritis, diabetes, heart disease and high blood pressure.

Protein

Your body cells are mostly made up of protein. Proteins are made up of lots of amino acids. We need protein to **repair** and **replace damaged cells** or to **make new cells during growth**.

These foods contain a lot of protein

Fats

Fats are made from fatty acids and glycerol. We need fats for a **store of energy**, to make **cell membranes** and for **warmth** (insulation).

Fat can also be bad for us. **Cholesterol** is a fatty deposit that can narrow arteries and contribute to heart disease.

Saturated fats increase blood cholesterol.

Monounsaturated fats have little effect and polyunsaturated fats may help reduce blood cholesterol.

These foods contain a lot of fat

Fibre

Fibre, or roughage, comes from plants. Fibre is not actually digested, but it keeps food moving smoothly through your system. It prevents constipation.

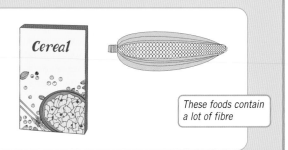

These foods contain a lot of fibre

Water

Water makes up approximately 65% of our body weight. Water is important because:

- our blood plasma is mainly water
- water is in sweat that cools us down
- chemical reactions in our cells take place in water
- waste products are removed from our bodies in water

The food and drink we consume contains water.

Vitamins and minerals

We only need these in small amounts, but they are essential for good health. Your body turns everything you eat, except fibre, into body tissue by billions of reactions that occur in your body. Vitamins and minerals are essential to this process. Vitamins are found in fruit, vegetables and cereals.

Fruit: a good source of vitamins and minerals

Salt is needed in small amounts in our diet. An adult, on average, needs about 6 g per day but actually consumes 60% more. Salt contains sodium which is linked to heart disease, high blood pressure and strokes.

In foods, 0.5 g of sodium is considered a lot, whereas 0.1 g is a little, so remember to read the food nutrition labels.

> **Remember, each individual's diet reflects their personal choice which may be influenced by their medical requirements or their religion.**

---

1. What do we use carbohydrates for?
2. What type of carbohydrate would long distance runners need to eat before a race?
3. In cold countries, what nutritional group is particularly important?
4. Why is protein important for our cells?
5. What type of fat could lower cholesterol?
6. What type of fat increases cholesterol levels in the blood?

The nervous system

The nervous system is in charge. It controls and co-ordinates the parts of your body so that they work together at the right time. The nervous system co-ordinates things you do not even think about, like breathing and blinking.

The central nervous system

The central nervous system (CNS) consists of the brain and spinal cord connected to different parts of the body by **nerves**. Your body's sense organs contain **receptors**. Receptors detect changes in the environment called stimuli.

Nose – sensitive to chemicals in the air.
Mouth – sensitive to chemicals in food.
Ears – sensitive to sound and balance.
Skin – sensitive to touch, pressure and temperature.
Eyes – sensitive to light.

The receptors send messages along nerves to the brain and spinal cord in response to stimuli from the environment. The messages are called **nerve impulses**. The CNS sends

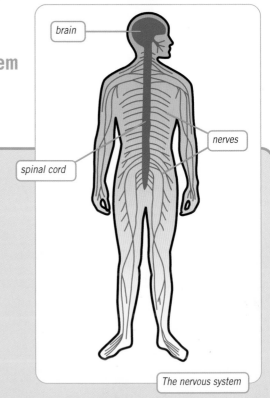

The nervous system

nerve impulses back along nerves to **effectors**, which bring about a response.

Effectors are muscles that bring about movement, or glands that secrete hormones.

💡 *Remember, receptors are your sense organs. Effectors are your muscles or glands.*

Nerves

Nerves are made up of nerve cells or **neurones**. There are three types of neurone: sensory, motor and relay neurones.

Neurones have a nucleus, cytoplasm and cell membrane, but they have changed their shape and become specialised.

The **sensory neurones** receive messages from the receptors and send them to the CNS.

The **motor neurones** send messages from the CNS to the effectors telling them what to do. Nerve impulses travel in **one direction only**. A **relay neurone** connects the sensory neurone to the motor neurone in the CNS.

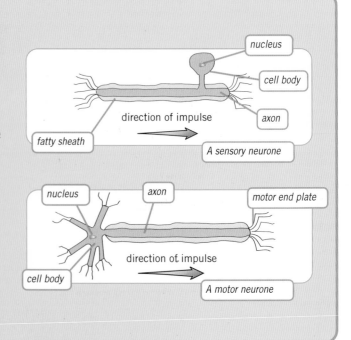

A sensory neurone

A motor neurone

Reflex and voluntary actions

Voluntary actions are things you have to think about – they are under conscious control. They have to be learned, like talking or writing.

Reflex actions produce rapid, involuntary responses and they often protect us and other animals from harm. Examples include reflex actions in a newborn baby, the pupils' response to light, knee-jerk reflex and blinking.

In certain circumstances, the brain can override a reflex response. For example, when holding a hot plate, the brain sends a message to the motor neurone in the reflex arc to keep hold of the plate and not to drop it.

The reflex arc

The reflex response to your CNS and back again can be shown in a diagram called the **reflex arc**.

1 Stimulus in this example is a sharp object.
2 The receptor is the pain sensor in the skin.
3 The nerve impulse travels along the sensory neurone.
4 The impulse is passed across a **synapse** to the relay neurone.
5 The impulse is passed across a synapse to the motor neurone.
6 The impulse is passed along a synapse to the muscle effector in the arm.
7 You move your hand away.

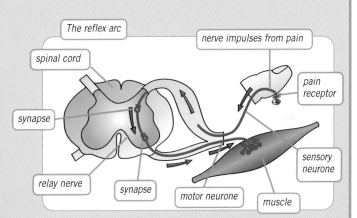

The reflex arc

spinal cord

nerve impulses from pain

synapse

pain receptor

relay nerve

synapse

motor neurone

muscle

sensory neurone

Whenever you respond to changes in your surroundings, your nervous system always follows this sequence of events:

stimulus → receptor → sensory neurone → relay neurone → motor neurone → effector → response

💡 *A synapse is a gap between two nerve cells. A chemical is released at the end of a synapse that starts an impulse in the next nerve cell. Synapses can be affected by drugs and alcohol.*

QUICK TEST

1 What does the CNS consist of?
2 What is a synapse?
3 Which neurone is connected to the effector?
4 What is a stimulus?

5 Why are reflex actions useful?
6 Name the five sense organs
7 Which neurone is connected to the receptor?

The eye

The eye is one of the human sense organs. Parts of the eye can control the amount of light entering it and other parts control focusing on near and distant objects.

Inside the eye

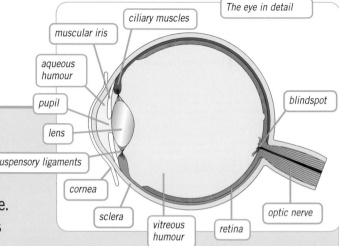

The eye in detail

ciliary muscles

muscular iris

aqueous humour

pupil

lens

suspensory ligaments

cornea

sclera

vitreous humour

retina

optic nerve

blindspot

Cornea – a transparent window in the front of the eye.

Sclera – the protective, white outer layer of the eye.

Muscular iris – controls how much light enters the eye and alters the shape of the pupil.

Pupil – a hole that allows light through (in front of the lens).

Lens – helps focus a picture. It is held in place by the suspensory ligaments and ciliary muscles. It can change shape.

Retina – contains light sensitive cells; rods for dim light, cones for colour. The retina sends nerve impulses to the brain.

Optic nerve – receives nerve impulses from the retina and sends them to the brain.

Ciliary muscles – change the thickness of the lens when focusing.

Suspensory ligaments – hold the lens in place.

🅘 *Make sure you can label the eye if given a diagram in the exam.*

🅘 *The cornea and lens work together to produce an image on the retina.*

Vision

Humans, and many hunting animals, have **binocular vision**. This means that our eyes are facing forward. Each eye has a slightly different perspective on a scene and this enables us to judge distances and depth effectively.

Cows, horses and other animals classed as prey have **monocular vision** – their eyes are on the side of their heads. This allows them to have a wider field of view and be aware of predators sneaking up on them.

Problems with vision

Short-sightedness results when the eyeball is too long. This means that light is focused too

far in front of the retina. Short-sighted people can see near objects but not distant ones.

Long-sightedness is when the eyeball is too short. Distant objects can be seen, but not ones close up.

Red-green colour blindness is an inherited condition that affects more males than females. It is caused by specialised cells in the retina, called cones, not functioning correctly. People with this condition cannot distinguish between red, green and yellow.

Adjusting to light and dark

Bright light

- Circular muscles contract.
- Radial muscles relax.
- The iris closes and makes the pupil **smaller**.
- Less light enters the eye.

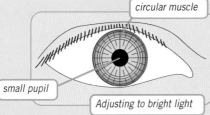

small pupil

circular muscle

Adjusting to bright light

Dim light

- Radial muscles contract.
- Circular muscles relax.
- The iris opens and makes the pupil **bigger**.
- More light enters the eye.

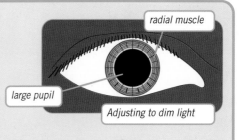

radial muscle

large pupil

Adjusting to dim light

> *Remember, the pupil in bright light gets smaller and in dim light, the pupil gets larger. The iris controls the size of the pupil.*

Seeing things

Light from an object enters the eye through the cornea.

The curved cornea and lens produce an image on the retina that is upside down.

The receptor cells in the retina send impulses to the brain along sensory neurones in the optic nerve. The brain interprets the image and you see the object the right way up.

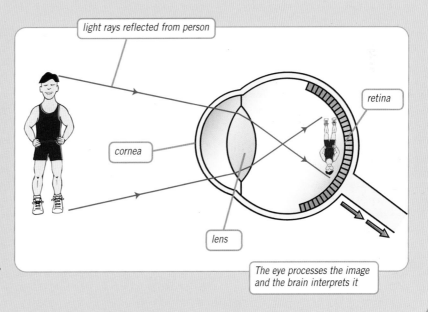

light rays reflected from person

cornea

lens

retina

The eye processes the image and the brain interprets it

1. Name the part of the eye that controls the amount of light entering it.

2. What happens to the size of the pupil in bright light?

3. What is the function of the optic nerve?

4. Which part of the eye does light enter through?

5. What is the difference between binocular vision and monocular vision?

6. What is the name of the hole in the middle of the iris?

7. What happens to the size of the pupil in dim light?

The brain

The brain is situated at the top of the spinal cord and is protected by the skull. The brain spinal cord and neurones make up the *central nervous system*. The brain co-ordinates different parts of the body to make them work together and bring about a correct response to a stimulus.

Parts of the brain

The cerebral cortex makes up the outer layer of the brain. In mammals, as with humans, it looks like it has many bumps and grooves. The cerebral cortex can be divided down the middle into two halves called the cerebral hemispheres. These are made up of lobes. Look at the diagram of the brain on the right to see which areas are responsible for each function.

The **medulla** is part of the brain that attaches to the spinal cord. It controls automatic actions such as breathing and heart rate. The **cerebellum** controls our co-ordination and balance.

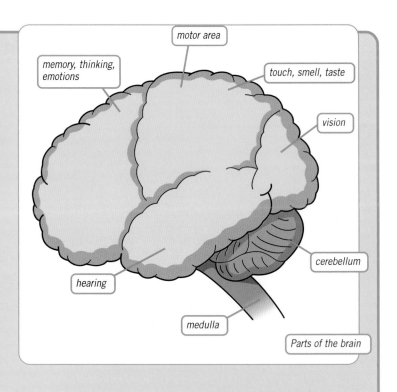

memory, thinking, emotions

motor area

touch, smell, taste

vision

cerebellum

hearing

medulla

Parts of the brain

The brain and learning

The brain works by sending electrical impulses received from the sense organs to the muscles. In mammals, the brain is complex and contains billions of neurones that allow learning by experience and behaviour.

The interaction between mammals and their environment results in nerve pathways forming in the brain. When mammals learn from experience, pathways in the brain become more likely to transmit impulses than others, which is why it is easier to learn through repetition.

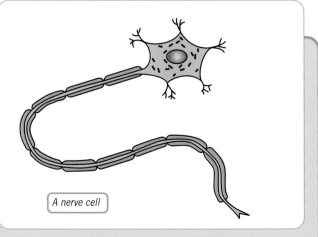

A nerve cell

The way in which we learn language is still being debated by linguists and child psychologists. Some say that there is a crucial period of language acquisition that ends when a child is around 12 years of age.

Disorders of the brain

Strokes are known as brain attacks and occur when the blood supply to the brain is stopped. The neurones start to die which leads to paralysis and loss of speech. The cause of a stroke is the blockage of blood vessels in the brain or the bursting of blood vessels leading to bleeding on the brain. Symptoms of a stroke include weakness/numbness in the face, leg, arm, one side of the body and loss of vision, difficulty speaking, headache and dizziness.

Strokes are linked to high blood pressure, smoking, heart disease and diabetes.

Epilepsy is the disruption of electrical activity in the brain which causes abnormal functioning. Sufferers have seizures that vary in severity. They prevent the brain from interpreting and processing signals such as sight, hearing and muscle control. **Grand mal seizures** start in one area of the brain and spread across. Sufferers have convulsions, twitches and loss of consciousness.

Petit mal seizures are non-convulsive. Sufferers become unaware of their surroundings and stare off into space or freeze.

Some of the causes of epilepsy include head injuries, strokes, brain tumours or infections such as meningitis. The attacks can be brought on by stress, lack of sleep, flashing lights or sounds and low blood sugar levels. There is no cure for epilepsy, only treatment with drugs or surgery, to control the seizures.

Parkinson's disease is a chronic progressive movement disorder in which the brain degenerates. The cause is unknown. It usually occurs over the age of 60. Symptoms include tremors, rigidity, slow movement, poor balance and difficulty walking.

Brain tumours are uncontrollable growths of cells. They can be **malignant** and cancerous, or **benign**. Benign tumours can still cause problems by putting pressure on the skull.

The causes of brain tumours are unknown, but the risks are increased by exposure to radiation or chemicals, and when the immune system is weakened through illness such as Aids. Brain tumours are more common in people over the age of 40, or children.

💡 *Look back at 'The nervous system' on page 6 and link it with the brain structure and function.*

Drugs and the brain

Drugs such as ecstasy, are known to affect thinking and memory in the brain. Ecstasy affects the transmission of impulses across synapses. It blocks the removal of a substance called serotonin, so serotonin levels build up in the brain which enhances a person's mood.

QUICK TEST

1. Which part of the brain controls breathing and heart rate?
2. What disorder disrupts the electrical activity of the brain?
3. What is a stroke?
4. How do we learn things?
5. Which part of the brain helps us keep our balance?
6. What do we call the outer layer of the brain?

Causes of disease

Microbes are bacteria, fungi and viruses. Not all microbes cause disease; some are useful. Microbes rapidly reproduce in warm conditions when there is plenty of food.

How are diseases spread?

Diseases are spread either:

- by **contact** with infected people, animals or objects used by infected people, e.g. athlete's foot, chickenpox and measles are spread through contact in this way
- through the **air**, e.g. flu, colds and pneumonia
- through infected **food and drink**, e.g. cholera from infected drinking water and salmonella from infected food.

air

food

touch

drink

Sources of disease

Remember that not all microbes are harmful and cause disease.

Cancer

Cancer occurs when body cells that are normally under control, grow out of control and become a mass of cells known as a tumour.

The most common cancer in men is prostate cancer. In most cases, if it is caught early enough, it can be cured. Breast cancer may affect up to 1 in 9 women in their life and 1% of males. It often runs in families.

Taking the contraceptive pill, obesity and heavy drinking may increase the risk.

Skin cancer is caused by overexposure to UV (ultraviolet) light from the sun. The use of sunbeds can also increase the risk.

Fungi

Fungi cause diseases such as athlete's foot and ringworm. Most fungi are useful as decomposers. Yeast is a fungus that is used when making bread, beer and wine.

Bacteria 1

Bacteria are living organisms that feed, move and carry out respiration.

How do bacteria cause disease?
Some bacteria **destroy living tissue**.

For example, tuberculosis (TB) destroys lung tissue. Bacteria can produce poisons, called **toxins**. Food poisoning is caused by bacteria releasing **toxins**.

Bacteria 2

Tuberculosis

Tuberculosis, or TB, is an infectious disease affecting the lungs. The bacteria destroys lung tissue. It is spread when sufferers of the disease cough and sneeze, causing other people to breathe in the bacterial TB. This disease was a major problem in the early 19th and 20th centuries.

In the 1940s, improvements to public health and the discovery in 1946 of an antibiotic to treat it, led to a decline of the infection. For a while, however, the guard was let down and incidences of the disease increased again in the 1980s, particularly as drug-resistant

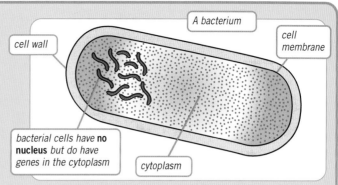

cell wall

A bacterium

cell membrane

bacterial cells have **no nucleus** but do have genes in the cytoplasm

cytoplasm

strains began to emerge. There are about 7000 reported cases of tuberculosis in the UK at present.

Treatment involves a course of antibiotics. Various antibiotics are used to prevent the bacteria from becoming resistant to one type. Schools have a vaccine called the BCG to prevent TB.

Viruses

Viruses consist of a **protein coat** surrounding a few **genes**.

Viruses are much smaller than bacteria.

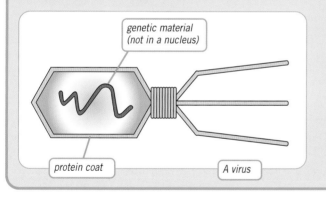

genetic material (not in a nucleus)

protein coat

A virus

They do not feed, move, respire or grow; they just reproduce. Viruses can only survive inside the cells of a living organism. They **reproduce inside the cells** and release thousands of new viruses to infect new cells.

They **kill the cell** in the process. Examples of diseases caused by viruses are HIV, flu, chickenpox and measles.

💡 *Learn the structure of a bacterium and a virus; notice the similarities and differences between these and general animal and plant cells.*

How do microbes get in?

Microbes have to enter our body before they can do any harm.

respiratory systems – droplets of moisture containing viruses are breathed in

digestive system – microbes get in via food and drink

skin – if the skin is damaged, microbes can get in

reproductive system – diseases can be passed on through sexual intercourse

Routes for microbes to enter the body

QUICK TEST

1. Name the three types of microbe.
2. How are infections spread?
3. Name four ways in which microbes can enter the body.
4. Name two diseases caused by viruses.
5. Name two diseases caused by bacteria.

Defence against disease

The human body has many methods of preventing microbes from entering the body. If microbes do get into the body, however, your immune system goes into action.

Prevention is better than cure

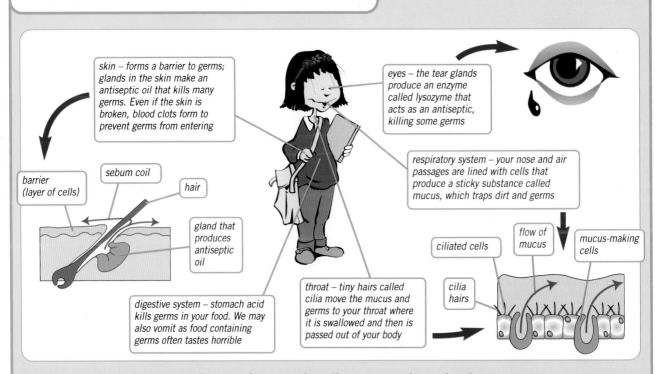

skin – forms a barrier to germs; glands in the skin make an antiseptic oil that kills many germs. Even if the skin is broken, blood clots form to prevent germs from entering

barrier (layer of cells)

sebum coil

hair

gland that produces antiseptic oil

digestive system – stomach acid kills germs in your food. We may also vomit as food containing germs often tastes horrible

throat – tiny hairs called cilia move the mucus and germs to your throat where it is swallowed and then is passed out of your body

eyes – the tear glands produce an enzyme called lysozyme that acts as an antiseptic, killing some germs

respiratory system – your nose and air passages are lined with cells that produce a sticky substance called mucus, which traps dirt and germs

ciliated cells

flow of mucus

mucus-making cells

cilia hairs

The human body has several ways of preventing disease-causing microbes from entering; these are called natural defences.

Antibiotics

Sometimes bacteria get through the body's defences and reproduce successfully. In this case, outside help in the form of **antibiotics** is needed to kill the germs. Antibiotics kill the germs without harming the body cells.

Penicillin was the first form of antibiotic. It is made from a mould called *Penicillium notatum*. **Antibiotics cannot treat infections caused by viruses**. The body has to fight them on its own. Antibiotics can kill most bacteria, but as we continue to use them, bacteria are becoming **resistant** to them.

There is a need for careful use of antibiotics as overuse has led to the highly resistant MRSA developing.

Drug testing

New drugs and medical treatments have to be extensively tested and trialled before being used. They are tested in the laboratory before being tested on human volunteers.

They are first tested on healthy volunteers to test for safety; and then on people with the illness to test for effectiveness.

The immune system response

If microbes get into your body, **white blood cells** spring into action. White blood cells make chemicals called **antitoxins** that destroy the toxins produced by bacteria. White blood cells called **phagocytes** engulf bacteria or viruses. If the microbes are in large numbers, however, the other type of white blood cell, called **lymphocytes**, are involved.

Germs have chemicals on their surface called **antigens**. Lymphocytes recognise these antigens as **foreign**. **Lymphocytes produce chemicals called antibodies** that attach to antigens and clump them together. **Phagocytes** then engulf and destroy the bacteria and viruses.

Artificial immunity

Artificial immunity involves the use of vaccines. **A vaccine contains dead or harmless germs**. These germs have antigens on them and your white blood cells respond to them as if they were alive by multiplying and producing antibodies. A vaccine is an advanced warning so that if germs of this type infect the person, the white blood cells can **respond immediately** and kill the germs.

Vaccinations are an example of **passive immunity** as they cause you to produce your own antibodies and fight the disease yourself.

An injection of ready-made antibodies is called **active immunity**.

The vaccine to treat MMR (measles, mumps and rubella) is a viral vaccine which has caused controversy because of the possible side effects of using a triple vaccine instead of three separate ones. All vaccines, in fact, carry the possibility of side effects.

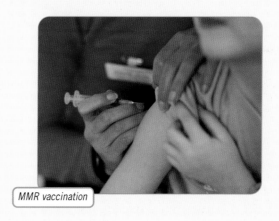

MMR vaccination

Natural immunity

Making antibodies takes time, which is why you feel ill at first and then get better as the disease is destroyed by the white blood cells and antibodies.

Once a particular antibody is made, it stays in your body. If the same disease enters your body, the antibodies are much quicker at destroying it and you feel no symptoms. **You are now immune to that disease**.

Make sure you know the difference between natural immunity and artificial immunity.

QUICK TEST

1. How does the skin protect against disease?
2. What is the job of mucus?
3. What chemicals do white blood cells produce?
4. What is the role of antibodies?
5. What are vaccines?

Drugs

Smoking and solvents damage health, without a doubt. Alcohol and drugs are also dangerous if misused, for either recreational or pharmaceutical purposes.

Drugs – why are they dangerous?

Drugs are powerful chemicals; they alter the way the body works, often without you realising it. **Drugs affect the brain and nervous system**, which in turn affect activities such as driving and behaviour. Drugs fall into four main groups: sedatives, painkillers, hallucinogens and stimulants.

Sedatives

These drugs **slow down the brain** and make you feel sleepy. Tranquillisers and sleeping pills are examples. They are often given to people suffering from anxiety and stress. These drugs seriously alter reaction times and give you poor judgement of speed and distances.

A drug alters, or inhibits, the way the body works

Painkillers

These drugs **suppress the pain sensors in the brain**. Paracetamol, Aspirin, heroin and morphine are examples. Heroin can be injected, which increases the risk of contracting HIV; it is also highly addictive.

Hallucinogens

These drugs **make you see or hear things that do not exist**. These are called hallucinations. Examples of hallucinogens are ecstasy, LSD and cannabis.

Stimulants

These drugs **speed up the brain and nervous system**, and make you more alert and awake.

Examples include amphetamines, cocaine and the less harmful caffeine in tea and coffee. Over-use results in high energy levels.

Drugs and the Law

Recently cannabis has become a 'class C drug', meaning there are now less harsh penalties for a person caught in possession of it. If, however, it is 'in possession with intent to supply', the penalty is up to 14 years imprisonment. The cannabis debate still continues about whether it is harmful, addictive and leads users on to using harder drugs such as heroin. At present, health professionals cannot agree.

Solvents

Solvent fumes are inhaled and are absorbed by the lungs. They soon reach the brain and **slow down breathing and heart rates**.

Solvents also damage the **kidneys and liver**. Repeated inhalation can cause loss of control and unconsciousness. Many first-time inhalers die from heart failure or suffocation if using aerosols.

Solvents, like glue and aerosols, reach the brain

Alcohol

Alcohol is a **depressant**. It reduces the activity of the brain and nervous system.

Alcohol is absorbed through the gut and taken to the brain in the blood. It damages neurones in the brain and causes irreversible brain damage. The liver breaks down alcohol at the rate of one unit an hour, but an excess of alcohol has a very **damaging effect on the liver**, **called cirrhosis**.

Each of these drinks contains one unit of alcohol

1 glass of sherry

½ pint cider (0.3 litre)

1 glass of wine

½ pint beer (0.3 litre)

1 single whisky

Smoking

Tobacco contains many harmful chemicals: **nicotine** is an addictive substance and a mild stimulant; **tar** is known to contain carcinogens that contribute to cancer; and **carbon monoxide** prevents red blood cells from carrying oxygen.

If a pregnant woman smokes, **carbon monoxide** deprives the foetus of oxygen and can lead to a low birth mass. Some diseases aggravated by smoking include **emphysema, bronchitis, heart and blood vessel problems and lung cancer**.

Scientific concept

The link between smoking and lung cancer is now becoming widely accepted. Tobacco contains carcinogens, chemicals that cause cancer. According to Cancer Research UK, it causes 9 out of 10 lung cancers.

Smoking: a proven cause of health problems

QUICK TEST

① Which parts of the body are affected by alcohol?

② Name three chemicals contained in tobacco.

③ What diseases does smoking cause?

④ What is the name of the disease of the liver?

⑤ How do stimulants affect the nervous system?

⑥ Why must you not take sedatives before driving?

Homeostasis and diabetes

- Homeostasis is the mechanism by which the body maintains a *constant internal environment*.
- Blood sugar levels are maintained by two hormones called glucagon and insulin.
- Diabetes is a disease caused by too little of the hormone insulin.

Diabetes

Diabetes results when the **pancreas does not make enough of the hormone insulin**. As a consequence, blood sugar levels rise and very little glucose is absorbed by the cells for respiration. This can make the sufferer tired and thirsty. If untreated, it leads to weight loss and even death.

Diabetes can be controlled in two ways.
1 **Attention to diet**. A special low-glucose diet is needed, and can be all that is required, to control some diabetes.

2 In more severe cases, diabetics have to **inject themselves with insulin** before meals. This causes the liver to convert the glucose into glycogen straight away, thus removing glucose from the blood.

Scientific concept

In 1920, Fred Banting and Charles Best discovered insulin as a treatment for diabetes. They extracted it from the pancreas and successfully treated diabetic dogs. We used to use pig's insulin to treat diabetes in humans.

Homeostasis

Examples of homeostasis include keeping the body temperature constant and controlling blood sugar levels. Information is passed to the brain, and the brain sends messages back to adjust the levels back to normal.

The kidney has a major role in homeostasis. It controls the amount of water in our body, as well as the removal of excess substances and the poisonous substance, urea.

Homeostasis involves many other organs of the body such as the skin and kidneys. They all work together to maintain internal conditions, such as balancing water loss with water gain, the ion content, and temperature.

The kidneys 1

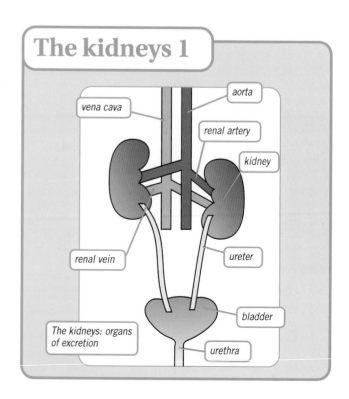

vena cava

aorta

renal artery

kidney

renal vein

ureter

bladder

urethra

The kidneys: organs of excretion

The kidneys 2

The kidneys are organs of **excretion**; they remove the waste product urea, excess water, and ions such as salt. They first **filter** the blood, then **reabsorb** what the body needs.

There are two kidneys and these are situated towards the back of the body, just above the waist.

Pancreas and homeostasis

The pancreas is an organ involved in homeostasis; it **maintains the level of glucose (sugar) in the blood** so that there is enough for respiration. The pancreas secretes two hormones into the blood: **insulin and glucagon**. If blood sugar levels are **too high**, which could be the case after a high carbohydrate meal, special cells in the pancreas detect these changes and release insulin. The **liver** responds to the amount of insulin in the blood by taking up glucose and **storing it as glycogen**. **Blood sugar levels return to normal**.

If blood sugar levels are **too low**, which could be the case during exercise, the pancreas secretes glucagon. Glucagon stimulates the **conversion of stored glycogen in the liver back into glucose**, which is then released into the blood. **Blood sugar levels return to normal**.

Remember, insulin lowers blood sugar levels and glucagon raises blood sugar levels.

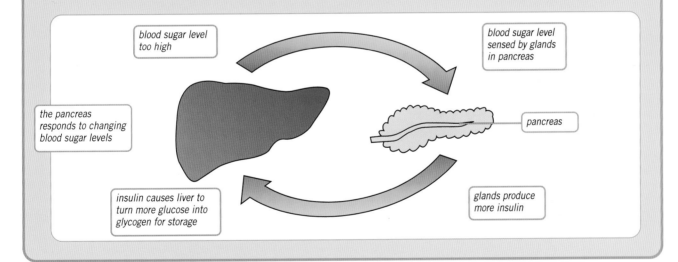

blood sugar level too high

blood sugar level sensed by glands in pancreas

pancreas

the pancreas responds to changing blood sugar levels

insulin causes liver to turn more glucose into glycogen for storage

glands produce more insulin

QUICK TEST

1. What two hormones does the pancreas produce?
2. What other organ is involved in controlling blood sugar levels?
3. Which hormone raises blood sugar levels?
4. Which hormone lowers blood sugar levels?
5. How can diabetes be treated?
6. What causes diabetes?
7. Where are the kidneys situated?

The menstrual cycle

Adolescence

Adolescence is a time in people's lives where the body changes from a child to an adult. Emotions can also change. Puberty is the first stage of adolescence and most changes occur at this time. Puberty usually begins between the ages of 10–14 in girls and a little older in boys. Not everybody starts puberty at the same time.

The menstrual cycle consists of a menstrual bleed and ovulation – the release of an egg. Hormones control the whole cycle.

Ovaries secrete the hormones progesterone and oestrogen.

Hormones

There are hormones associated with changes that occur during puberty. The female sex hormones are oestrogen and progesterone. The male hormone is testosterone.

The male and female sex hormones control characteristics during puberty. In males, their voices break, they develop hair on their face and body, the genitals develop and sperm production begins. In females, the breasts develop, they grow hair under the arms and pubic hair, and menstruation starts.

The menstrual cycle 1

A sequence of events occurs each month in females called the menstrual cycle. The menstrual cycle lasts approximately **28 days**. The menstrual cycle involves preparing the uterus to receive a fertilised egg. If fertilisation does not happen, then the egg and the lining of the uterus break down and leave the body through the vagina. This is sometimes called having a **period** and lasts between **four** and **seven** days.

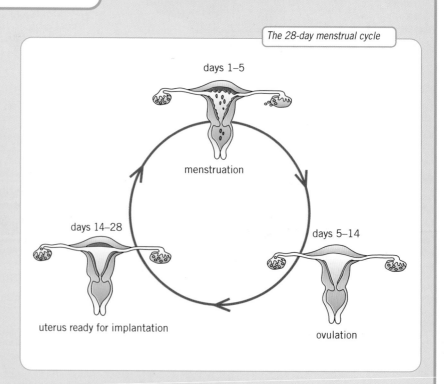

The 28-day menstrual cycle

days 1–5

menstruation

days 14–28

days 5–14

uterus ready for implantation

ovulation

The menstrual cycle 2

The stages of the menstrual cycle

Days 1–5 – a menstrual bleed (a period) occurs: the lining of the uterus breaks down. Caused by lack of **progesterone**.

Days 5–14 – oestrogen is released from the ovaries and the uterus lining builds up again. Oestrogen also stimulates egg development and release of the egg from the ovaries – called **ovulation**.

Days 14–28 – **progesterone** is released which maintains the uterus lining. If no fertilisation occurs then **progesterone production stops**.

Days 28–5 – the cycle begins again.

Controlling fertility

Fertility in women can be controlled in two ways:

1 A hormone called FSH (follicle stimulating hormone) stimulates eggs to mature in the ovaries. FSH can be administered as a **'fertility drug'** to women whose own production is too low to stimulate eggs to mature. This can result in multiple births.

2 Oestrogen can be used as an **oral contraceptive** to inhibit eggs maturing.

IVF (In vitro fertilisation) is a treatment for infertile couples. It involves extracting the eggs and sperm and fertilising them outside the body. The cells that develop are then implanted in the womb for growth and development into an embryo.

Be prepared to evaluate the benefits and problems associated with the use of hormones to control fertility. For example, do they interfere with nature? Or are the possible side-effects they may cause a risk worth taking?

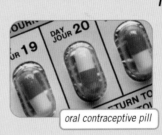

oral contraceptive pill

QUICK TEST

1. Where are the hormones oestrogen and progesterone made?

2. From where are the eggs released?

3. Which two hormones maintain the uterus lining?

4. What is ovulation?

5. What hormone can be used in oral contraceptives?

6. On what days does the menstrual bleed usually take place?

7. What causes the uterus lining to break down?

Genetics and variation

All living things vary in the way they look and behave. Variation can be between species or within species. Living things that belong to the same species are all slightly different.

Genetics, the environment or a combination of both may cause these differences.

Genes, chromosomes and DNA

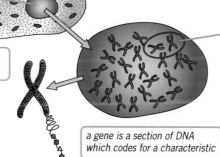

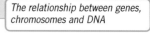

The relationship between genes, chromosomes and DNA

each nucleus contains thread-like chromosomes

each chromosome is made up of a long-stranded molecule called DNA

proteins and enzymes control all our characteristics; genes are chemical instructions that code for a particular protein or enzyme and therefore our characteristics

the chromosomes occur in pairs, one from the mother and one from the father, we have 46 chromosomes in our body cells

a gene is a section of DNA which codes for a characteristic

there is a pair of genes for each feature. We call the different versions of a gene alleles

Genetic variation

Why do we look like we do? The answer is because we have inherited our characteristics from our parents. Brothers and sisters are not exactly the same as each other because they inherit different genes from their parents. It is completely random. There are thousands of different genes in every human cell, so the combination of genes in a cell is endless; the chance of two people having the same genes is virtually impossible. Identical twins are an exception as their genes are identical. Even identical twins, however, are not completely identical; this is due to **environmental factors**.

Genetic variation occurs within species

Variation in plants

Plants are affected more than animals by small changes in the environment. Sunlight, temperature, moisture level and type of soil are factors that will determine how well a plant grows. A plant grown in sunlight will grow much faster and may double in size compared to a plant grown in the shade, whereas a dog living in England would show no significant changes if it moved to Africa.

The growth of plants can vary in response to environmental factors such as sunshine

Variation in animals

We vary because of the random way our genes are **inherited**. The environment can affect most of our characteristics. It is usually a combination of genetics and environment that determines how we look and behave. Just how significant the environment is in determining our features is difficult to assess; for example, is being good at sport inherited or is it due to your upbringing? There are some characteristics that are not affected by the environment at all:

1 Eye colour
2 Natural hair colour
3 Blood group
4 Inherited diseases

A lot of the questions on this topic involve your opinion, for example, on whether being good at sport is due to genetics or environment. Just make sure you can discuss both sides of the argument.

Are differences due to the environment?

We can **produce clones** of plants by taking cuttings. The cuttings are genetically identical to each other. We can then grow the plants in different conditions. Any differences in their appearance would be due to the environment.

If you could not produce clones and wanted to test whether the differences were due to environmental or genetic reasons, then you could:

- Replant them in a different place to see if they then grow more alike. If they do, it is the environment that has caused the difference.
- Plant two plants of the same species in the same conditions to see if the environment has caused the differences again.

Environmental variation

The environment is your surroundings and all the things that may affect your upbringing. Identical twins may be separated at birth and grow up in totally different surroundings, following different diets for example. Any differences between the twins must be due to the environment they were brought up in as they have identical genes.

Many of the differences between people are caused by a **combination** of genetic and environmental influences.

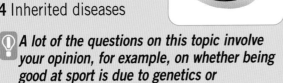

QUICK TEST

1. Is having a scar environmental or inherited?
2. Why do animals and plants of the same species vary?
3. Where are chromosomes found?
4. How many chromosomes are there in a human body cell?
5. Name four environmental factors that determine the growth of plants?
6. Is blood group inherited or caused by the environment?

Genetics

Genetics is the study of how information is passed on from generation to generation. Genetic diagrams are used to show how certain characteristics are passed on.

Genetic engineering is the process in which genes from one organism are removed and inserted into the cells of another. It has many exciting possibilities, but is not without its problems. Scientists can now genetically modify plants and animals using the process of genetic engineering.

Mendel's experiments

Gregor Mendel, an Austrian monk, discovered the principle behind genetics by studying the inheritance of a single factor in pea plants. The inheritance of single characteristics is called **monohybrid inheritance**.

Definitions

Recessive means it is the weaker allele. **Dominant** means it is the stronger allele. The **genotype** of red pea plants could be RR or Rr. Although the genotypes are different they are still red because red is dominant. The **phenotype** is what the organism physically looks like.

A worked example – inheritance of eye colour

Remember, we have two alleles for eye colour, one from each parent, making up a gene.

- The allele for brown eyes is **dominant**, so it can be represented by the letter 'B'.
- The allele for blue eyes is **recessive** so it is represented by the letter 'b'.
- A mother and father both have the genotype Bb.

What colour eyes will their children have? We can show the possible outcomes using a **Punnett square**. This gives a 3:1 ratio of brown to blue eyes.

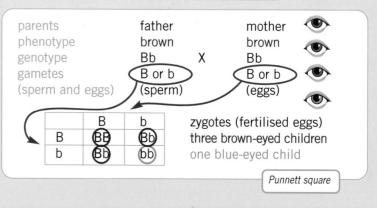

parents		father		mother	
phenotype		brown		brown	
genotype		Bb	X	Bb	
gametes (sperm and eggs)		B or b (sperm)		B or b (eggs)	

	B	b
B	BB	Bb
b	Bb	bb

zygotes (fertilised eggs)
three brown-eyed children
one blue-eyed child

Punnett square

Different combinations of genotypes can be crossed and the outcomes worked out in the same way using a Punnett square.

- For example, what would happen if the mother was genotype (Bb) and the father was genotype (bb)?
- This gives a 1:1 ratio of brown eyes to blue eyes.

Remember, the ratios are only probabilities and may not always happen.

Manipulating genes

Our genes are a code for particular proteins that enable all our normal life processes to function. **Many diseases are caused when the body cannot make a particular protein**.

Genetic engineering has been used to treat diabetic people through the production of the protein, insulin. The gene that codes for insulin can be found in human pancreas cells. Other human proteins made in this way include the human-growth hormone that is used to treat children who do not grow properly.

Gene therapy

It may be possible to use genetic engineering to treat inherited diseases such as **cystic fibrosis**. Sufferers could be cured if the correct gene is inserted into their body cells. The problem that exists with cystic fibrosis is that the cells that need the correct gene are in many parts of the body, which makes it difficult to remove them to insert the required gene.

Another problem is that even if the correct gene is inserted into the body cells, the cells would not multiply. This means that there would be many cells that still have the faulty gene.

The benefits of genetic engineering

Genetic engineering benefits industry, medicine and agriculture in many ways.

We have developed plants that are resistant to pests and diseases, and plants that can grow in adverse environmental conditions.

Tomatoes and other sorts of fruit are now able to stay fresher for longer. Animals are engineered to produce chemicals in their milk, such as drugs and human antibodies. The list seems endless and there are no doubts as to the benefits of genetic engineering now and in the future, but there are also risks and moral issues that are associated with this relatively modern technology.

Tomatoes can be genetically engineered to stay fresh longer by inserting a gene from fish into their cells. Would you eat one?

Genetics questions are a good way to gain marks, as long as you show all your working and label everything as you go along.

QUICK TEST

1. What does recessive mean?
2. What does dominant mean?
3. What are gametes?
4. What does monohybrid inheritance mean?
5. What could be the genotypes of a brown-eyed child if brown was the dominant characteristic?
6. Does a person with blue eyes have a genotype bb of a phenotype bb?

Inherited diseases

Not all diseases are caused by microbes. Genes pass on characteristics from one generation to the next. Sometimes 'faulty' genes are inherited that cause diseases.

Cystic fibrosis

Causes

Cystic fibrosis is the commonest inherited disease in Britain; about one in 2000 children born in Britain has cystic fibrosis. Cystic fibrosis is caused by a **recessive allele** (c), carried by about one person in 20. People who are **heterozygous** with the genotype (Cc) are said to be **carriers**. They have no ill effects. Only people who are homozygous for this allele (cc) are affected.

- Heterozygous means having two different alleles
- Homozygous means having two alleles the same.

Symptoms

Cystic fibrosis sufferers produce large amounts of **thick**, **sticky mucus** that can block air passages and digestive tubes. They have difficulty breathing and absorbing food. The mucus slows down the exchange of oxygen and carbon dioxide between the lungs and blood. The mucus also **encourages bacteria to grow**, which cause chest infections.

Treatment

There is still no cure; treatment involves **physiotherapy** to try to remove some of the mucus and **strong antibiotics** to treat the infections. It was only in 1989 that the gene that causes cystic fibrosis was discovered. This allowed a test to be developed, which can tell if a person is a carrier by analysing their DNA. If a couple know that they are both carriers they have a difficult decision to make. **A genetic counsellor** can explain to them that there is a one in four chance of having a child with cystic fibrosis. They then have to decide if the risk of having children is too great.

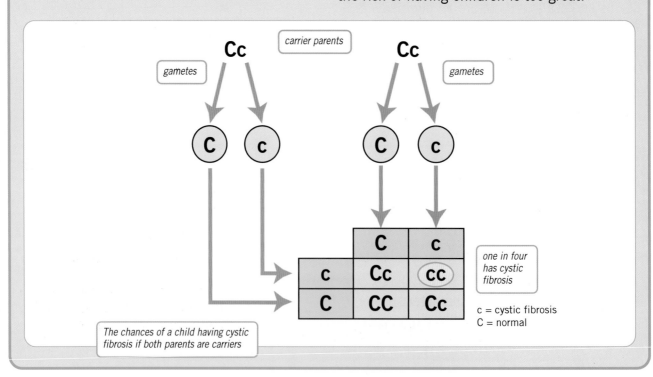

The chances of a child having cystic fibrosis if both parents are carriers

carrier parents

gametes

one in four has cystic fibrosis

c = cystic fibrosis
C = normal

Huntington's chorea

Causes

Huntington's chorea is caused by a **dominant allele** (H). This means only one allele is needed to pass on the disease, so all **heterozygous people are sufferers (Hh)**. The only people free from the disease are **homozygous recessive (hh)**. It affects one in 20 000 people, so is a rare disease. There is a 50% chance of inheriting the disease if just one parent is a carrier.

Symptoms

The brain degenerates and the sufferer has uncontrolled, jerky movements.
The sufferer becomes moody and depressed and their memory is affected.

Treatment

There is no cure. Onset of the disease is late; the sufferer is about 30–40 years old before

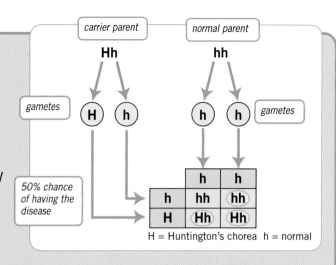

		h	h
	h	hh	hh
	H	Hh	Hh

H = Huntington's chorea   h = normal

they realise that they have it. Consequently, many have already had children and passed on the disease.

> Remember, cystic fibrosis is caused by a recessive allele and Huntington's chorea by a dominant allele.

Stem cell therapy

Stem cell therapy is undergoing research as a treatment of human disease and organ failure. Stem cells refer to cells that have yet to specialise into different types of tissue. They are found in adult bone marrow or human embryos and the umbilical cord. Adult stem cells do not have the same potential as embryonic stem cells to treat illness.

The idea is that stem cells have the ability to divide and specialise into any tissue needed, such as nerve cells.

Stem cell therapy research and use is still in the early stages and requires much more funding, support and regulation particularly when the stem cells involved are from donated human embryos. There is an ethical dilemma concerning the moral and legal status of the human embryo.

Scientific concept

The potential for stem cell therapy is endless as it can be used to replace tissue that has lost its function, for example to correct heart problems. It can also be used to treat genetic diseases as the stem cells can be implanted into the donor before the genetic disease has developed.

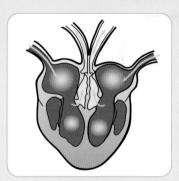

QUICK TEST

1. How is cystic fibrosis inherited?
2. What are the symptoms of cystic fibrosis?
3. What are stem cells?
4. Where are stem cells found?
5. Why are the chances of inheriting Huntington's chorea so high if just one parent is a carrier?

Selective breeding

People are always trying to breed animals and plants with special characteristics. For example, a fast racehorse or a cow that produces lots of milk. This is called *selective breeding* or atificial selection.

Artificial selection

The procedures involved in artificial selection are:

- Select the individuals with the best characteristics.
- Breed them together using sexual reproduction.
- Hopefully, some of the offspring will have inherited some of the desirable features; the best offspring are selected and are bred together.
- This is repeated over generations until the offspring have all the desired characteristics.

Learn the four steps involved in selective breeding and remember, it is also called artificial selection.

Selective breeding in animals

- Cows have been selectively bred to produce a greater quantity of milk.
- Beef cattle have been bred to produce better meat.

The problem with only breeding from the best cows and bulls is that the cows can only give birth once a year. New techniques have therefore been developed such as embryo transplants.

Selective breeding in plants

Selectively bred individuals may not always produce the desired characteristics as **sexual reproduction always produces variation**. With plants this can be overcome by producing clones. **Clones are genetically identical individuals**. To produce clones, asexual reproduction is needed.

Problems with selective breeding

The problem is a **reduction in the number of alleles in a population**. If animals or plants are continually bred from the same best animals or plants, the animals and plants will all be very similar. If there is a change in the environment, the new animals and plants may not be able to cope with it. There may be no alleles left to breed new varieties of plants and animals selectively. It is important to keep wild varieties alive, to maintain species variation.

Embryo transplants

The process is as follows:

1 Sperm is taken from the best bull.
2 The best cow is given hormones to stimulate the production of lots of eggs.
3 The eggs are removed from the cow and are fertilised in a petri dish.
4 The embryos are allowed to develop, but are then split apart to form clones before they become specialised.
5 The embryos are then implanted into other cows called surrogates, where they grow into offspring.

Advantages: the sperm and the eggs can be frozen to be used at a later date; a large number of offspring can be produced from one bull and one cow.

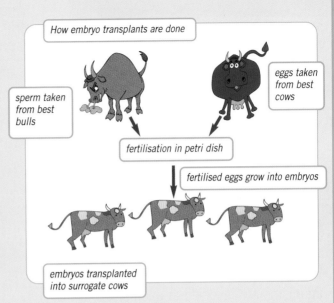

How embryo transplants are done

sperm taken from best bulls

eggs taken from best cows

fertilisation in petri dish

fertilised eggs grow into embryos

embryos transplanted into surrogate cows

Tissue culture and cuttings

Gardeners can produce new, identical plants by **taking cuttings** from an original parent plant. The plants are dipped in rooting powder containing hormones and are kept in a damp atmosphere to grow into new plants. The new plants would be clones.

Tissue culture is a technique used by commercial plant breeders. They take just a few plant cells and grow a new plant from them, using a special growth medium containing hormones. The advantages are that new plants can be grown quickly and cheaply all year round, with special properties such as resistance to diseases. Plants also reproduce sexually, attracting insects for pollination. The resulting plants show **variation**.

From cuttings to clones

trim off lower leaves and make a slanting cut just below a leaf stalk

roots grow from stem after several weeks in water and hormone powder

Scientific concept
Dolly the sheep was the first mammal cloned in 1996. She died prematurely in 2003. Her early death fuelled the debate about long-term health problems of clones.

Make sure you can list the advantages of selective breeding and also the disadvantages.

QUICK TEST

1 What is selective breeding?
2 What is the difference between artificial selection and natural selection?
3 What are clones?
4 Name two methods of selective breeding in plants.
5 What is the main disadvantage of selective breeding?

Pyramids

Before looking at pyramids, you need to recall the following:

- A food chain shows us simply who eats who, whereas a food web is a series of linked food chains that gives us a more realistic picture.

- Energy enters food chains when plants absorb sunlight during photosynthesis, so the Sun's energy actually supports all life on Earth.

Pyramids of numbers

A pyramid of numbers tells us how many organisms are involved at each stage in the food chain. At each level of the food chain (trophic level) the number of organisms generally gets less.

fox
rabbit
grass

A pyramid of numbers shows the number of organisms involved at each stage

Sometimes a pyramid of numbers does not look like a pyramid at all as it does not take into account the **size** of the organisms.

blackbird
ladybirds
aphids
rose bush

A rose bush counts as one organism, so the bottom level is small, but it can still support many herbivores.

fleas
fox
rabbits
lettuce

A pyramid of numbers can look nothing like a pyramid. In this pyramid of numbers, the top carnivores are fleas that feed on a single fox.

Pyramids of biomass

A biomass pyramid takes into account the **mass of each organism**. If we take the information from the pyramid of numbers and multiply it by the organism's mass then we get a pyramid shape again.

A single rose bush weighs more than the aphids and lots of aphids weigh more than the few ladybirds that feed on them. Finally, a blackbird weighs less than the many ladybirds it feeds on.

blackbird
ladybirds
aphids
rose bush

A biomass pyramid takes account of the mass of each organism.

Loss of energy in food chains 1

Food chains rarely have more than four or five links in them. This is because **energy is lost along the way**. The final organism is only getting a fraction of the energy that was produced at the beginning of the food chain.

Plants absorb energy from the Sun. Only a small fraction of this energy is converted into glucose during photosynthesis. Some energy is lost to decomposers as plants shed their leaves, seeds or fruit. The plant uses some energy during respiration and growth.

Loss of energy in food chains 2

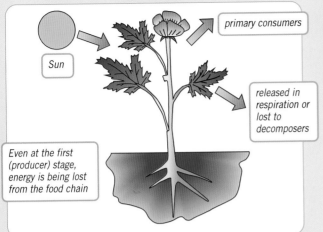

Sun

primary consumers

released in respiration or lost to decomposers

Even at the first (producer) stage, energy is being lost from the food chain

The plants biomass increases, which provides food for the herbivores. Only approximately 10% of the original energy from the Sun is passed on to the primary consumer in the plants biomass. The primary consumer also has energy losses and only approximately 10% of their total energy intake is passed on to the secondary consumer.

Where does the energy go?

The 90% energy loss at each stage goes on life processes such as **respiration**. Respiration

releases heat energy to the surroundings. Animals that are warm blooded use up a lot of energy in **keeping warm**, so they need to eat a lot more food.

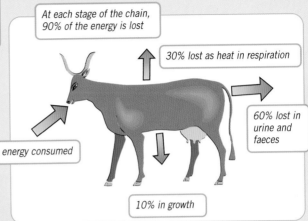

At each stage of the chain, 90% of the energy is lost

30% lost as heat in respiration

60% lost in urine and faeces

energy consumed

10% in growth

As you can see from the diagram of energy transfers in the cow, a lot of energy is lost in **urine and faeces. Not all of the organism's body mass is eaten**. From a farmer's perspective, growing a field of wheat is cheaper than rearing a field of beef cattle as the energy losses incurred with the cattle would be greater.

Efficiency of food production

As so much energy is lost along food chains, we must look at ways to improve the efficiency of food production and reduce losses. There are two ways this can be done.

1 **Reduce the number of stages in the food chain**. It is more energy efficient to eat plant produce than meat.
2 **Intensively rear animals**. Restrict their movement, keep them warm, and they will

not need feeding as much; use antibiotics to keep disease at bay.

> *A common exam question is about the energy losses in food chains and how to reduce them, so make sure you learn them thoroughly.*

> *There is always competition for resources in a food web, try to imagine what effect a change in one organism's numbers will have on the rest of the food web.*

QUICK TEST

① Why do food chains only have four or five links?

② What do pyramids of numbers show?

③ What pyramids can be drawn using the mass of animals and plants?

④ Where does a plant get its original energy source?

⑤ List the ways that energy is lost in food chains.

⑥ How can we reduce energy loss in foood chains?

Evolution

Evolution is all about change and improvement from simple life forms. The theory of evolution states that all living things that exist today or once existed, evolved from simple life forms three billion years ago. Natural selection is the process that causes evolution. Fossils provide the evidence for evolution.

The theory of evolution – from animal to human

The theory of evolution

Natural selection, as demonstrated in the wild

there is a struggle for existence

organisms produce a large number of offspring

in any species there is a variation between individuals

organisms with useful characteristics are more likely to survive and pass them on to the next generation

Religious theories are based on the need for a 'creator' for all life to exist on earth, but there are other theories.

Charles Darwin, a British naturalist, first put forward his theory about 140 years ago. Charles visited the Galapagos Islands off the coast of South America and made a number of observations.

1 Organisms produce more offspring than could possibly survive.

2 Population numbers remain fairly constant despite this.

3 All organisms in a species show **variation**.

4 Some of these variations are inherited.

He also concluded from these observations that since there were more offspring produced than could survive, there must be a struggle for existence. This led to the strongest and fittest offspring surviving and passing on their genes to their offspring. This is sometimes called the **'survival of the fittest' or natural selection**.

Natural selection

Darwin stated that the process of natural selection was the basis for evolution. **Only those who can adapt to suit their new environment survive to breed and pass on their advantageous genes.**

Natural selection in action 1

An example of where the environment has caused changes in a species is the **peppered moth**. They live in woodlands on lichen-covered trees. There are two types of peppered moth, a light, speckled form and a dark form. The dark-coloured moth was caused by a mutation and was usually eaten by predators. In the 1850s, the dark type of moth was rare but pollution from factories started to blacken tree trunks. The dark moth was then at an advantage because it was camouflaged.

Natural selection in action 2

dark-coloured moth against a
soot-covered tree

the pale moth is at a
disadvantage in polluted areas

Pollution played a key role in the 'survival of the fittest' for these peppered moths

By 1895, most of the population of moths were dark. In cleaner areas, the light moth had an advantage against predators so it survived to breed.

Fossils

Fossils are the remains of dead organisms that lived millions of years ago. They are found in rocks. Most dead organisms decay and disintegrate, but the following are ways that fossils can be formed.

1 The hard parts of animals that do not decay, form into a rock.

2 Minerals which preserve their shape gradually replace the softer parts of animals that decay very slowly.

3 Fossils are formed in areas where one or more of the conditions needed for decay are absent, for example, areas where there is **no oxygen, moisture or warmth**.

Fossils provide evidence for evolution. They are preserved in rock with generally the younger fossils being found near the surface. The evolution of the horse is clearly shown by fossils. Natural selection has operated to produce the modern horse.

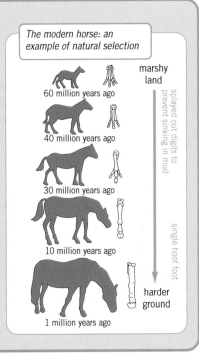

The modern horse: an example of natural selection

60 million years ago
40 million years ago
30 million years ago
10 million years ago
1 million years ago

marshy land
splayed out digits to prevent sinking in mud
single hoof foot
harder ground

Extinction

Species that are unable to adapt to their surroundings become extinct. Examples include the mammoth, the dodo, and sabretoothed tiger. Extinction can also be caused by changes in the environment, new predators, new disease, new competition, or human activity such as hunting, pollution or habitat destruction.

It is not only natural selection that can lead to a new species forming. Selective breeding, mutations and genetic engineering also play a part in the formation of new species.

Scientific concept

Darwin's theory became widely accepted eventually, but a man called Lamarck suggested that animals evolved features according to how much they used them. His theory stated, for example, that giraffes grew longer necks because they needed to reach food.

QUICK TEST

1 Who were the two scientists that put forward their theories of evolution?

2 Which individuals would survive a change in the environment?

3 What process causes evolution?

4 What conditions need to be absent for fossils to be formed?

5 What was Darwin's observation when he looked at the individuals in a species?

Adaptation and competition

Animals and plants have to adapt in order to survive in a habitat. In a habitat, there is always competition between species and within species for communal resources and this keeps population numbers in check.

Sizes of populations

Population numbers cannot keep growing out of control; factors that keep the population from becoming too large are called **limiting factors**. The factors that affect the size of a population are:

- the amount of food and water available
- predators or grazing – as they may eat the animal or plant
- disease

- climate, temperature, floods, droughts and storms
- competition for space, mates, light, food and water
- human activity, such as pollution or destruction of habitats
- suitable conditions as organisms will only live and reproduce where these exist.

Adaptation

A polar bear has adapted to living in cold, arctic regions of the world.

- It has a **thick coat** to keep in body heat as well as a **layer of blubber** for insulation.
- Its coat is **white** so that it can blend into its surroundings.
- Its **fur is greasy** so it doesn't hold water after swimming. This prevents cooling by evaporation.
- A polar bear has **big feet** to spread its weight on snow and ice; it also has big, **sharp claws** to catch fish.
- It is a **good swimmer** and **runner** to catch prey.
- The shape of a polar bear is **compact** even though it is large. This keeps the surface area to a minimum to reduce body heat.

The polar bear: adapted to deal with Arctic conditions

A camel has features that enable it to survive in the hot deserts of the world.

The camel: ideally suited to living in hot, dry deserts

- The camel has an ability to **drink** a lot of water and **store** it.
- It loses very little water as it produces **little urine** and it can cope with big changes in temperature so there is **no need for sweating**.
- All fat is stored in the humps so there is **no insulation layer**.
- Its **sandy** colour provides **camouflage**.
- It has a **large surface area** to enable it to lose heat.

> *The adaptations of a camel and polar bear are just two examples. There are many more forms of adaptation found in animals and plants.*

Competition

As populations grow, there may be overcrowding and limited resources to support the growing numbers. Animals have to compete for **space, food and water** in their struggle to survive. Only the strongest will survive, which leads to the survival of the fittest.

Plants compete for **space, light, water and nutrients**.

Predator/prey graphs

In a community, the numbers of animals stay fairly constant. This is partly due to the amount of food limiting the size of the populations. A **predator** is an animal who hunts and kills another animal. A **prey** is the hunted animal.

Populations of predator and prey go in cycles.

1 If the population of prey increases, then there is more food for the predator, so its numbers increase.

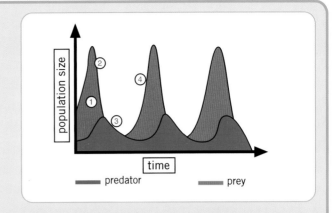

2 This causes the number of prey to decrease as they are eaten.

3 This, in turn, causes the number of predators to decrease, as there is not enough food and they compete with each other.

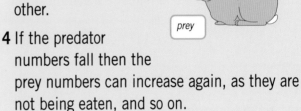

predator

prey

4 If the predator numbers fall then the prey numbers can increase again, as they are not being eaten, and so on.

Some key terms

- A **habitat** is where an organism lives; it has the conditions needed for an organism to survive.
- A **community** consists of living things in the **habitat**.
- Each **community** is made up of different **populations of animals and plants**.

- Each **population** is adapted to live in that particular **habitat**.
- An **ecosystem** is formed from all the living things and their physical environment.

QUICK TEST

1. What is a habitat?
2. Define the word community.
3. What things do animals compete for?
4. What things do plants compete for?
5. What factor determines whether animals or plants survive in their environment?

6. If the number of prey increases, what will happen to the numbers or predators?
7. How does a polar bear's coat help it survive in the Arctic?

Environmental damage 1

Improvements in agriculture, health and medicine have meant a dramatic rise in human populations. An increase in population size leads to an increase in pollution and higher demands on the world's resources.

Effects on the environment

Humans are using up the Earth's resources, including fossil fuels, at an alarming rate.

Burning fossil fuels contributes to acid rain and the greenhouse effect by releasing harmful gases into the air.

Gases such as sulphur dioxide dissolve in rain and make it acidic. Acid rain damages wildlife and pollutes rivers and lakes. Carbon dioxide is also released into the atmosphere by burning fossil fuels. This gas traps heat inside the Earth's atmosphere and causes the temperature of the Earth to increase. This is known as the **greenhouse effect**.

Fertilisers

Plants need nutrients to grow, which they take up from the soil. With intensive farming methods, nutrients are quickly used up, so the farmer has to replace them with artificial fertilisers. Fertilisers enable farmers to produce more crops in a smaller area of land, and can reduce the need to destroy the countryside for extra space. They can, however, cause problems if they leak into rivers and streams.

Deforestation

In the UK, there are not many forests left. In underdeveloped countries, people are chopping down forests to provide timber or space for agriculture, to try to provide for the growing numbers of people. This causes several problems to the environment.

Burning this timber **increases the level of carbon dioxide in the air**. Forests absorb carbon dioxide in the air and provide us with oxygen. Chopping down trees leads to **soil erosion** as the soil is exposed to rain and wind. Water evaporates from trees into the air, so without the trees there will be a **decrease in rainfall**. Destroying forests also **destroys many different animal and plant habitats**.

Intensive farming

Farming has had to become more intensive to try and provide more food from a given area of land. Intensive farming, such as fish farming and battery farming, can produce more food, but they have their problems. Many people regard intensive farming of animals as cruel. In order to produce more food from the land, **fertilisers and pesticides** are needed.

Learn arguments for and against intensive farming.

Destruction of the land

What can be done?

The problems will get worse unless people can learn to limit their needs and therefore prevent the destruction of our planet. Intensive farming does produce quality food, more than enough to supply people's needs in Europe, but it also creates many problems.

An increase in industry has led to the need to take over more land, which destroys wildlife and causes pollution

we use land for building

dumping our rubbish

getting raw materials

farming to feed the world

A possible solution to some of the problems is **organic farming**. Organic farming produces less food per area of land and can be expensive, but it attempts to leave the countryside as it is and is kinder to animals. Organic farming uses **manure as a fertiliser, sets aside land** to allow wild plants and animals to flourish and uses biological control of pests. Biological control of pests is the use of other animals to eat pests; it is not as effective as using chemicals but produces no harmful effects.

Another method for reducing harm to the environment is to use greenhouses to grow food efficiently and out of season. We can also look at developing alternative energy sources, such as solar power and wind energy. This will help conserve the world's rapidly diminishing fossil fuel supply.

Do not forget about acid rain and the greenhouse effect as problems have intensified with the growing human population.

1. Why has the human population increased in last few hundred years?

2. What is deforestation?

3. How does deforestation contribute to the greenhouse effect?

4. What other problems does deforestation cause?

5. What could be used as an alternative to fertilisers?

6. Name ways in which we can reduce harmful effects on the environment.

Environmental damage 2

Our Earth is in danger because of the harmful effects of pollutants on air, water and land. Humans are responsible for the destruction of our planet and unless we do something about it, serious harm will come to the Earth and all who live here.

Pollution

A pollutant is a substance that harms living things – animals, plants and humans. Pollutants can spread through the air, water and soil. There are animals and plants called **indicator species** which, in their absence or presence, indicate pollution. For example, in polluted water, invertebrate animals such as the sludge worm and water louse are present.

In areas of high air pollution, certain species of algae and lichen grow.

Pollution of the air

Burning fossil fuels is the main cause of atmospheric pollution. Factories and cars use fossil fuels. They release **carbon dioxide**, which contributes to the **greenhouse effect**; and **sulphur dioxide** and **nitrogen oxides**, which cause **acid rain**.

Smoke from burning fossil fuels contains particles of soot (carbon) which can blacken buildings and collect on plants preventing them from photosynthesising.

Remember that carbon dioxide contributes to the greenhouse effect; and sulphur dioxide and nitrogen oxides contribute to acid rain.

Pollution of the soil and water

Fertilisers and pesticides used on land can be washed into rivers and seas causing damage to wildlife. Factory waste and sewage are often dumped at sea. Oil spillages at sea are also a problem to marine life and seabirds as well as ruining beaches.

Acid rain

Burning fossil fuels is the main cause of acid rain. The gases **sulphur dioxide** and **various nitrogen oxides** are released. They dissolve in water vapour in the clouds and fall as acid rain. Acid rain kills fish and trees, and damages buildings.

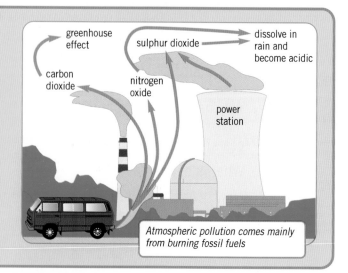

Atmospheric pollution comes mainly from burning fossil fuels

The greenhouse effect

Evidence is being generated that shows that the world is warming up. This is called **global warming** and is caused by the **greenhouse effect**.

The temperature of the Earth is kept in balance by the heat we get from the Sun and the heat that is radiated back into the atmosphere. Carbon dioxide and water vapour act like an insulating layer (like glass in a greenhouse) and **trap and keep** some of the heat from the Sun. This is **natural global warming** and it provides enough heat for living things.

The levels of carbon dioxide are increasing because of the burning of fossil fuels and the cutting down of trees (which absorb carbon dioxide). This increase in carbon dioxide is trapping too much heat and the Earth's temperature is slowly rising above normal.

Methane gas is also contributing to the greenhouse effect. Methane is produced naturally from cattle waste and rice fields.

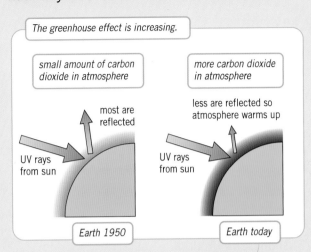

The greenhouse effect is increasing.

small amount of carbon dioxide in atmosphere

more carbon dioxide in atmosphere

most are reflected

less are reflected so atmosphere warms up

UV rays from sun

UV rays from sun

Earth 1950

Earth today

Problems caused by the greenhouse effect include changes in temperature which could cause **melting of the polar ice caps** and **raised sea levels**. Serious **flooding** could result. Plants may be killed by the warming, and weeds may thrive as they grow well on extra carbon dioxide.

Conservation and sustainable development

With the human population increasing and using up resources, we need to find a way of keeping a quality of life for future generations. This is known as sustainable development.

It is important to protect our food supply, maintain biodiversity and conserve resources as we do not know what the future may hold. Animals have already become extinct and many are in danger, such as the red squirrel, osprey and the whale. We need to look at ways of protecting habitats; breeding endangered species in captivity to increase numbers; and giving these species legal protection.

A way to maintain fish stocks and our woodland is to introduce quotas and replant woodland.

QUICK TEST

1. What is the main cause of atmospheric pollution?
2. What gases cause acid rain?
3. What damage does acid rain cause?
4. Why is the Earth warming up?
5. Which two gases cause the greenhouse effect?
6. What are the problems caused by the greenhouse effect?

Ecology and classification

We are surrounded by a huge variety of living organisms in a variety of habitats. Ecology is the study of living things in their habitats.

In any habitat, the numbers of organisms is usually large. Therefore, we use sampling techniques to see what organisms live there and then we can estimate the population size.

Different types of keys can be used to identify animals and plants.

Sampling techniques

Quadrats

- A quadrat is a wooden or metal frame usually $1m^2$ in area.
- A quadrat is placed randomly in a field, for example, and the numbers of plants belonging to a species are counted within the quadrat.
- If the same is done 10 times, we can estimate the number of plants belonging to that species in the field.

Example method

1 Add up the number of daisies in 10 quadrats e.g. 30.

2 Divide by 10 to find the average per quadrat e.g. 0.3.

3 If the total area of the field is 500 m x 500 m = 250 000 m^2 and one square metre has 3 daisies, then the whole field will have 3 x 250 000 = 750 000 daisies.

Remember, this is only an estimate but is better than counting all the daisies by hand!

> *The areas sampled may be unrepresentative of the whole area so it is important to take into account the limitations of these methods.*

Pooters and pitfall traps

Counting plants is relatively easy, but insects tend to move around. Pooters can be used to collect insects and then identify them. Pitfall traps can be used to get an idea of the number of insects in a habitat.

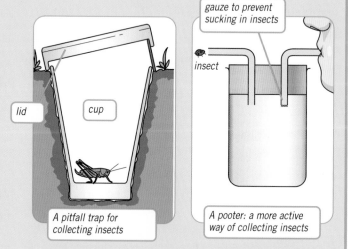

A pitfall trap for collecting insects

A pooter: a more active way of collecting insects

> *To get the bigger picture when sampling habitats, it is important to collect information on abiotic factors (physical) such as temperature, pH of soil and light intensity as these will affect where organisms live.*

Keys 1

When animals and plants have been collected in a sample, we can use keys to identify them.

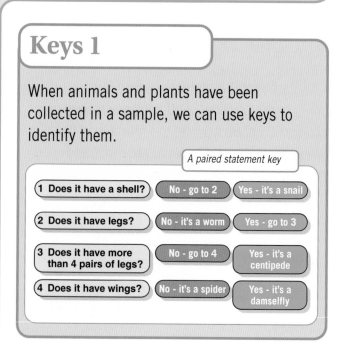

A paired statement key

1 Does it have a shell?	No - go to 2	Yes - it's a snail
2 Does it have legs?	No - it's a worm	Yes - go to 3
3 Does it have more than 4 pairs of legs?	No - go to 4	Yes - it's a centipede
4 Does it have wings?	No - it's a spider	Yes - it's a damselfly

Keys 2

A branching key

Has it got legs?
- Yes → Has it got wings?
  - Yes → **Damselfly**
  - No → Does it have more than four pairs of legs?
    - Yes → **Centipede**
    - No → **Spider**
- No → Has it got a shell?
  - Yes → **Snail**
  - No → **Worm**

Classification

Classification is a way of sorting living things into groups according to their similarities and differences. Carl Linnaeus devised a classification system based on features including body shape, types of limbs, and skeleton. The smallest group of living things is called a species and the largest are called kingdoms.

This is the order of classification:

Kingdom Phylum Class Order Family Genus Species

Species

A species is a group of living things that are able to breed together to produce fertile offspring. Species contain animals or plants that have several features in common but do show variation, for example different breeds of dog.

Different species can still be very similar and live in similar types of habitat. They may share a common ancestor. An example is the Galapagos finches studied by Charles Darwin. He studied different varieties of finches and concluded that they shared a common ancestor.

Ecosystems

There are natural ecosystems, such as woodland or lakes; and artificial ecosystems, such as greenhouses and aquariums.

However, they had evolved into different species because some had lived and adapted to different habitats by flying to various islands around the mainland.

Kingdoms

For many years, only two major kingdoms were recognised: the animal and plant kingdoms. Today scientists recognise five kingdoms. For many years fungi were classified as plants – but they now belong in their own kingdom, as they do not have chlorophyll and cannot make their own food by photosynthesis.

The animal kingdom is divided into vertebrates (animals with backbones) and invertebrates (animals without backbones).

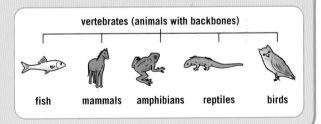

vertebrates (animals with backbones)

fish   mammals   amphibians   reptiles   birds

QUICK TEST

1. What are abiotic factors?
2. Who devised the classification system?
3. How many kingdoms exist today?
4. What name is given to the smallest group of living things?
5. To what group do animals with a backbone belong?

Practice questions

Use the questions to test your progress. Check your answers on page 124.

1. What is an indicator species?

....

2. Give an example of an intensive farming method.

....

3. What are reflex actions?

....

4. What was Dolly the sheep?

....

5. What was Mendel famous for?

....

6. How is the bacterial disease tuberculosis spread?

....

7. What organ of the body is affected by TB?

....

8. What is meant by the term 'active immunity'?

....

9. If you were to eat a diet rich in saturated fats what could the effects be?

....

10. What do the letters CNS stand for and what does it consist of?

....

11. Name the three types of neurone.

....

12. If a person had a grand mal seizure what disorder of the brain would they suffer from?

....

13. Which hormone used to be extracted from a pig's pancreas?

....

14. What is the function of:

a) insulin

....

b) glucagon?

....

15. Who discovered insulin?

....

16. What was the first type of antibiotic called?.

....

17. Name the two types of white blood cell that protect us from disease.

....

18. Explain the term 'natural immunity'.

....

19. Define the word homeostasis.

....

20. Name a recessive inherited disease and a dominant inherited disease.

....

21. What are alternative forms of a gene called?

....

22. Which hormones are involved in the menstrual cycle?

....

23. What type of organisms do we use for genetic engineering?

....

24. What information does a pyramid of biomass tell us?

....

25. Who developed the theory of evolution that we use today?

....

26. Who developed an alternative theory of evolution?

....

27. List some ways in which energy is lost from a food chain.

....

28. Name three ways of sampling habitats.

....

29. What system did Carl Linnaeus develop?

....

30. Define the word species.

....

Limestone

Limestone is a sedimentary rock.

If limestone is powdered, it can be used to neutralise the acidity in lakes caused by acid rain and to neutralise acidic soils.

Heating limestone

When **limestone** (calcium carbonate) is heated it breaks down to form **quicklime** (calcium oxide) and **carbon dioxide**.

> calcium carbonate → calcium oxide + carbon dioxide

This is an example of a **thermal decomposition** reaction.

Quicklime (calcium oxide) can be reacted with water to form **slaked lime (calcium hydroxide)**. A solution of slaked lime is known as limewater.

Reaction summary

> calcium oxide + water → calcium hydroxide

💡 *Calcium oxide and calcium hydroxide are both bases, so they can be used to neutralise acidic lakes and soils.*

The **thermal decomposition** of limestone is an example of a reaction that takes in heat energy. This is called an **endothermic reaction**.

The formula for limestone, $CaCO_3$, shows us the type and ratio of atoms present. In $CaCO_3$, the calcium, carbon and oxygen atoms are present in the ratio 1:1:3.

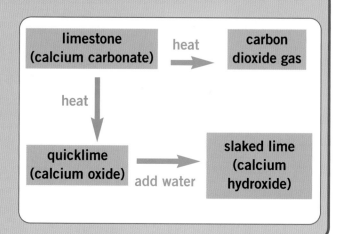

Similar thermal decomposition reactions

Other metal carbonates decompose in a **similar way** when they are heated. When copper carbonate is heated it breaks down to give copper oxide and carbon dioxide.

> copper carbonate → copper oxide + carbon dioxide

Heating baking powder

When **metal hydrogen carbonate compounds** are heated, they undergo thermal decomposition

reactions to form **metal carbonates, carbon dioxide and water**.

The main chemical compound in baking powder is sodium hydrogen carbonate, $NaHCO_3$. When heated fiercely it decomposes to form sodium carbonate, carbon dioxide and water.

> sodium hydrogen carbonate → sodium carbonate + carbon dioxide + water

Other uses of limestone

Limestone can be used to make other useful materials.

Cement

Cement is produced by **roasting powdered clay with powdered limestone** in a rotating kiln. If water is added and the mixture is allowed to set, it forms the hard, stone-like material cement.

Mortar

When **water is mixed with cement and sand,** then allowed to set, mortar is made.

Concrete

Concrete is made by **mixing cement, sand and rock chippings with water**. When water is added to cement, it hydrates and binds together all the particles to form a material that is as hard as rock. Concrete is hard and cheap and is widely used in building.

Glass

Glass can be made by **heating up a mixture of limestone (calcium carbonate), sand (silicon dioxide) and soda (sodium carbonate)** until the mixture melts.

QUICK TEST

❶ What is the main chemical in limestone?

❷ What is powdered limestone used for?

❸ Give the word equation for the thermal decomposition of zinc carbonate.

❹ What does 'endothermic' mean?

❺ How is cement made?

❻ How is glass made?

❼ Name the three products formed by the thermal decomposition of sodium hydrogen carbonate.

❽ What type of rock is limestone?

❾ Name the three products formed by the thermal decomposition of sodium hydrogen carbonate.

Fuels

Fuels are burnt to release energy. In this country, the fossil fuels coal, oil and gas are widely used. The burning of fuels is an exothermic reaction.

Formation of coal, oil and gas

Fossil fuels are formed over **millions of years** from the fossilised remains of dead plants and animals. When plants and animals die, they fall to the sea or swamp floor. Occasionally, the remains are covered by sediment very quickly. In the absence of oxygen, the remains do not decay. Over time, more layers of sediment gradually build up and the lower layers become heated and pressurised. Over millions of years, fossil fuels form but they are non renewable. Although they take many years to form, they are being used up very quickly.

💡 *Coal is mainly carbon. Petrol, diesel and oil are hydrocarbons.*

Fractional distillation of crude oil 1

Like many natural substances, crude oil is a **mixture**. In fact, it is a mixture of many substances, but the most important are called **hydrocarbons**. Hydrocarbons are molecules that only contain carbon and hydrogen atoms. Some of the hydrocarbons have very short chains of carbon atoms.

These hydrocarbons:

- are runny
- are easy to ignite
- have low boiling points
- are valuable fuels.

Other hydrocarbon molecules have much longer chains of carbon atoms. These hydrocarbon molecules:

- are more viscous (less runny)
- are harder to ignite
- have higher boiling points.

These longer hydrocarbon molecules are less useful as fuels. Before any of these hydrocarbon molecules can be used, however, they must first be separated into groups of molecules with a similar number of carbon atoms called **fractions**.

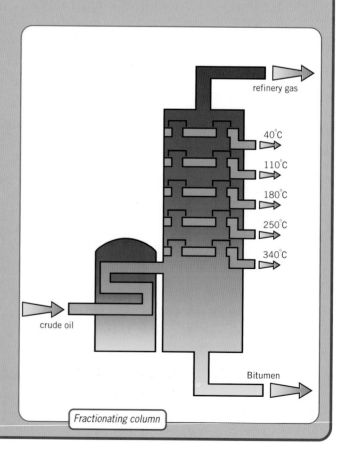

Fractionating column

Fractional distillation of crude oil 2

Crude oil can be separated by **fractional distillation**. First the crude oil is heated until it entually evaporates. The diagram of the fractionating column shows that the bottom of the column is much hotter than the top of the column. This means that short hydrocarbon molecules can reach the top of the column before they condense and are collected. Longer hydrocarbon molecules condense at higher temperatures and are collected at different points down the column.

How a fractionating column works

No. of carbon atoms in hydrogen chain	Temperature	Fraction collected
3	less than 40°C	refinery gas
8	40°C	petrol
10	110°C	naphtha
15	180°C	kerosene
20	250°C	diesel
35	340°C	oil
50+	above 340°C	bitumen

Cracking

The large hydrocarbon molecules separated during the fractional distillation of crude oil are not very useful. These hydrocarbon molecules, however, can be broken down into smaller, more useful and more valuable molecules by a process called **cracking**.

Industrial cracking

- The cracking of long chain hydrocarbons is carried out on a large scale.
- First, the long hydrocarbon molecules are heated until they evaporate.
- The vapour is then passed over a hot aluminium oxide catalyst.
- In this example, decane is being cracked to produce octane and ethene.

Octane is one of the hydrocarbon molecules in petrol. **Ethene**, which is a member of the **alkene family** of hydrocarbons, is also produced. Ethene is used to make a range of new compounds including plastics and industrial alcohol.

> *Cracking is an example of a thermal decomposition reaction. Some of the products of the cracking are very useful fuels.*

decane $C_{10}H_{22}$ (from the naphtha fraction) →   octane C_8H_{18} + ethene C_2H_4

Cracking large hydrocarbon molecules can produce more useful products. Some of these molecules are used as fuels

❶ Name three fossil fuels.

❷ How long does it take for fossil fuels to form?

❸ Which elements are found in hydrocarbon molecules?

❹ Give three properties of short chain hydrocarbon molecules.

❺ What is a hydrocarbon fraction?

❻ What family does ethene belong to?

Organic families

Carbon atoms have the ability to form four bonds with other atoms. This means that carbon atoms can be made into a large range of compounds. These compounds are the basis of life and the chemistry of these compounds is called organic chemistry.

Alkanes

The alkanes are a family of **hydrocarbon molecules**. This means that alkanes only contain hydrogen and carbon atoms. Scientists describe alkanes as **saturated** hydrocarbons. This is because they contain no C=C bonds so they already contain the maximum number of hydrogen atoms.

Alkanes are useful fuels, but as they do not contain C=C double bonds, they do not react with bromine water.

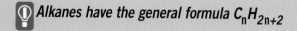 *Alkanes have the general formula C_nH_{2n+2}*

Name	methane	ethane	propane	butane
Chemical formula	CH_4	C_2H_6	C_3H_8	C_4H_{10}
Structure	H H–C–H H	H H H–C–C–H H H	H H H H–C–C–C–H H H H	H H H H H–C–C–C–C–H H H H H

Alkenes

The alkenes are also hydrocarbon molecules. Scientists describe alkenes as **unsaturated** hydrocarbons because they all contain one or more C=C double bond.

Alkenes are more reactive than alkanes due to the presence of C=C double bonds. This means alkenes are more useful because they

can be used to make new substances. Alkenes react with **bromine water**. Bromine water decolourises in the presence of alkenes.

Alkenes have the general formula C_nH_{2n}

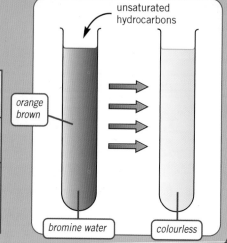

unsaturated hydrocarbons

orange brown

bromine water   colourless

Name	ethene	propene
Chemical formula	C_2H_4	C_3H_6

Structure	H H
	  C=C
	H H
		H H
		  C=C–C–H
		H H H

Alcohols

The term alcohol is often used for the compound **ethanol**. In fact, ethanol is just one member of a family of organic compounds called alcohols. All alcohols have an **–OH group**. Each member of the family differs from the previous one by the addition of a CH_2 group.

Name	methane	ethane
Chemical formula	CH_3OH	C_2H_5OH
Structure	H | H–C–O–H | H	H H | | H–C–C–O–H | | H H

Covalent bonding

All of these compounds contain covalent bonds.

Covalent bonding involves the sharing of electrons. The shared pairs of electrons hold the atoms together.

Carboxylic acids

Carboxylic acids are another family of organic compounds. All carboxylic acids have the functional group **–COOH**. Carboxylic acids are week acids. They react with metals, alkalis and metal carbonates. Carboxylic acids have rather unpleasant smells. The well known carboxylic acid, ethanoic acid, is found in vinegar.

The carboxylic acid, ethanoic acid, is found in vinegar

Esters

Esters are a family of organic compounds formed when alcohols react with carboxylic acids. Esters have **pleasant fruity smells and flavours** and are used widely in cheap perfumes and to flavour foods.

QUICK TEST

❶ How many bonds do carbon atoms form?

❷ Why are alkanes described as saturated hydrocarbons?

❸ What is the name of the first member of the alkane family?

❹ Draw the structure of the first four members of the alkane family.

❺ Draw the structure of the first two members of the alkene family.

❻ To which family does ethene belong?

❼ How could you differentiate between an alkane and an alkene?

❽ What is the general formula for an alkane?

❾ To which hydrocarbon family does the compound ethanol belong?

❿ What is the formula for ethanol?

Vegetable oils

Plant oils are a valuable source of energy in our diets. They are also essential sources of vitamins A and D. Vegetable oils can be produced from the fruits, seeds or nuts of some plants. Popular vegetable oils include olive oil and sunflower oil.

Vegetable oils can be extracted from the fruits, seeds and nuts of some plants. The oil is removed by crushing up the plant material and then collecting the oil

What is a fat molecule?

Fats and oils are complex molecules.

Saturated and unsaturated fats

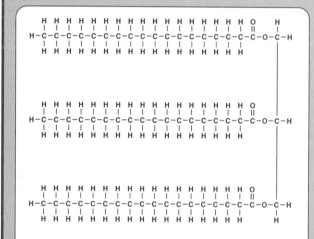

This is a molecule of a common animal fat

Animal fats are usually **solid**, or nearly solid, at room temperature. A saturated fat contains many C-C bonds but **no C=C** bonds. Scientists believe that people who eat lots of saturated fats may develop raised blood cholesterol levels, which is linked with an increased risk of heart disease. Most vegetable fats are liquids at room temperature so they are described as oils.

Vegetable oils contain C=C bonds. Scientists describe these molecules as unsaturated fats because they could hold more hydrogen atoms. The presence of the C=C bonds affects the way that the fatty acids in the molecule can pack together.

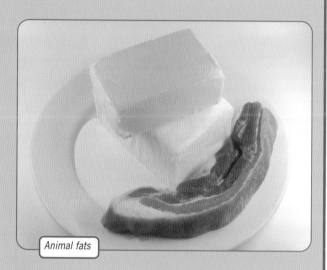

Animal fats

The C=C bonds are rigid and their presence causes kinks so that the fatty acids cannot pack closely together. Unsaturated fats have **lower melting points** than saturated fats. While most vegetable fats are **liquid at room temperature**, most animal fats are solids.

This is a molecule of a common vegetable oil

Hydrogenated vegetable oils

Vegetable oils are often liquids at room temperature because they contain C=C bonds. There are, however, advantages to using fats that are solid at room temperature – they are easier to spread.

Vegetable oils can be made solid at room temperature by a process known as **hydrogenation**. The oils are heated with **hydrogen and a nickel catalyst**. The hydrogen atoms add across double bonds to form fats that are solid at room temperature.

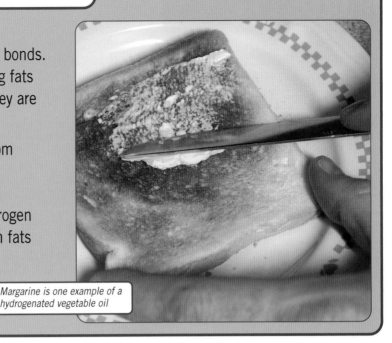

Margarine is one example of a hydrogenated vegetable oil

Emulsions

Salad dressing is an example of a type of everyday mixture called an **emulsion**. It is a **mixture of two liquids**: oil and vinegar. Salad dressing is made by shaking the oil and vinegar so that they mix together. After a short while, however, the oil and vinegar **separate out to form two distinct layers**. Many of the salad dressings bought from shops contain molecules called emulsifiers that help the oil and vinegar to stay mixed together. Emulsifiers are molecules which have two very different ends. One end is attracted to oil, while the other end is attracted to the water in the vinegar. The addition of emulsifiers keeps the two liquids mixed together.

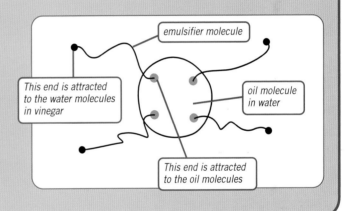

emulsifier molecule

This end is attracted to the water molecules in vinegar

oil molecule in water

This end is attracted to the oil molecules

Polyunsaturated fats

Some unsaturated fats have just one C=C bond in the fatty acid chain. These are described as mono-unsaturated fats.

Other unsaturated fats have **many C=C bonds**. These are known as **polyunsaturated fats**.

QUICK TEST

① From which parts of plants can we obtain oils?

② Which part of a sunflower is used to obtain oil?

③ Which vitamins do we obtain from eating fats?

④ Why is frying food faster than boiling food?

⑤ If a fat is a solid at room temperature, do you expect it to be saturated or unsaturated?

⑥ What is one advantage of having fats that are at room temperature?

Plastics

Many small molecules can be joined together to make one big molecule.

Polymerisation

We have seen how the simplest alkene, **ethene**, can be formed by the cracking of large hydrocarbon molecules. If ethene is heated under pressure in the presence of a catalyst, many ethene molecules can join together to form a larger molecule called poly(ethene) or **polythene**.

Here we can see how a large number of ethene molecules join together to form polythene.

The small starting molecules, in this case the ethene molecules, are called **monomers**.

The C=C bonds in the ethene molecules join together to form long chain molecules called **polymers**. A polymer, therefore, is made from lots of monomer units, in fact 'poly' means many. This is an example of an addition polymerisation reaction. The ethene molecules have simply joined together.

Other polymers

Polymerisation reactions may involve other monomer units. The exact properties of the polymer formed depend upon:

- the monomers involved
- the conditions under which it was made.

Polypropene
Polypropene is made by an additional polymerisation reaction between **many propene molecules**.

Many propene molecules join together to form polypropene

Polyvinyl chloride (PVC)
Polyvinyl chloride is made by an additional polymerisation reaction between **many**

chloroethene molecules. Chloroethene used to be called vinyl chloride.

Many chloroethene (vinyl chloride) molecules join together to form polyvinyl chloride

Polytetrafluoroethene (PTFE or Teflon)
Polytetrafluoroethene is made by an additional polymerisation reaction between **many tetrafluoroethene** molecules.

Many tetrafluoroethene molecules join together to form polytetrafluoroethene (PTFE)

Thermoplastics and thermosetting plastics

Thermoplastics consist of long polymer chains with **few cross-links**.

When heated, these chains untangle and the material softens. **It can then be reshaped**. On cooling, the material becomes solid and stiff again. Thermoplastics can be heated and reshaped many times. Polythene is a thermoplastic.

Thermosetting plastics consist of long, **heavily cross-linked** polymer chains. Once cooled, these plastics cannot be reshaped.

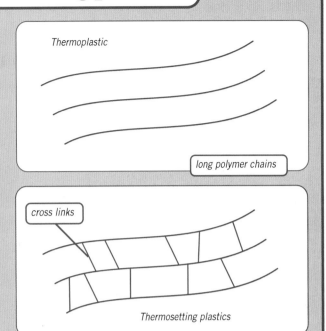

Thermoplastic

long polymer chains

cross links

Thermosetting plastics

New polymers

Scientists are developing new and exciting polymers.

Hydrogels are an example of these new types of polymers. Hydrogels are able to bind water and are being used to make special wound dressings to help injured people. Hydrogels help to:

- stop fluid loss from the wound
- absorb bacteria and odour molecules
- cool and cushion the wound
- reduce the number of times the wound has to be disturbed – the hydrogel is transparent so that doctors and nurses can

monitor the wound without having to remove the dressing.

Know the properties and uses of different plastics.

Scientific process

The problems caused by plastics that do not break down in the environment have encouraged scientists to design new biodegradable plastics.

QUICK TEST

1. Draw diagrams to show how polythene is formed from ethene.
2. Draw diagrams to show how polypropene is formed from propene.
3. What type of reaction is involved in the formation of polythene?
4. What is the name given to the small units that join together to form a polymer?
5. Which group of plastics have many cross-links?
6. What is the name of the polymer made from chloroethene molecules?

Ethanol

Ethanol is a member of the alcohol family of organic compounds.

Uses of ethanol

Ethanol has this structure:

H−C−C−O−H

with H and H above the first two carbons and H and H below.

The structure of ethanol

It is found in drinks like beer and wine and, in large amounts, it is toxic. Ethanol has many useful properties. It is a **good solvent** and evaporates quickly. Many aftershaves contain ethanol. Ethanol is an important raw material and can also be used as a **fuel**.

Methanol is another member of the alcohol group and it is even more toxic than ethanol.

Ethanol as fuel

In some countries, sugar beet or sugar cane is made into alcohol. This alcohol can then be mixed with petrol to produce a fuel for vehicles like cars. Ethanol is a **renewable energy** resource which burns very cleanly. **Alcohols**, however, **release less energy** than petrol when they are burnt. In order to produce enough alcohol for fuel, large areas of fertile land are required to grow the plants needed to produce the alcohol.

Sugar cane can be used to produce alcohol, which can be burnt as a fuel

Fermentation

Fermentation has been used to make alcohol for thousands of years. We use fermentation to make alcoholic drinks. Fruits, vegetables and cereals are all sources of the sugar glucose.

During fermentation, **yeast** is used to catalyse (speed up) the reaction in which glucose is converted into ethanol and carbon dioxide.

>   yeast
>
> glucose ➔ ethanol + carbon dioxide

The temperature of the reaction has to be carefully controlled. If the temperature falls too low, the yeast becomes inactive and the rate of the reaction slows down. If the temperature is too high, the yeast's enzymes are denatured and stop working altogether or the yeast may be killed.

💡 *Yeast is an enzyme or biological catalyst. It speeds up the conversion of sugar to alcohol and carbon dioxide, but is not itself used up in the process.*

fermentation lock

The fermentation lock allows carbon dioxide to escape, but stops oxygen in the air from reaching the alcohol. This is important, as ethanol can be easily oxidised to ethanoic acid which would make the drink taste sour.

An alternative process to fermentation

There is another, more modern way of producing vast amounts of alcohol. With this method, **ethene** (which is produced during the cracking of long-chain hydrocarbons) is **reacted with steam to produce ethanol**.

> ethene + steam ➔ ethanol

A catalyst of **phosphoric acid and a temperature of 300°C** are used.

This method of producing ethanol is much cheaper than fermentation. Our reserves of fossil fuels, however, are finite and they will run out one day.

QUICK TEST

❶ What family does ethanol belong to?

❷ Give three uses of ethanol.

❸ What is the name of the alcohol mixture used as a fuel in some countries?

❹ What is the catalyst used in fermentation?

❺ What type of compound is glucose?

❻ What happens to yeast if the temperature is too high?

Evolution of the atmosphere

The composition of today's atmosphere is:

- about 80% nitrogen
- about 20% oxygen
- plus small amounts of other gases, such as carbon dioxide, water vapour and noble gases (e.g. argon).

This has not always been the case, however.

Formation of the atmosphere

The first billion years
- During the first billion years of the Earth's life, there was **enormous volcanic activity**.
- The volcanoes belched out carbon dioxide, steam, ammonia and methane.
- The atmosphere was **mainly carbon dioxide** and there was very little oxygen. In fact, the Earth's early atmosphere was very similar to the modern day atmospheres of the planets **Mars and Venus**.
- The steam condensed to form the early oceans.

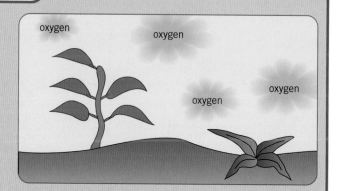

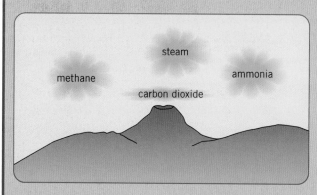

Later
- During the next two billion years, **plants evolved** and began to cover the surface of the Earth.
- The plants grew very well in the carbon dioxide rich atmosphere. They steadily removed carbon dioxide and produced oxygen.

Later still
- Most of the carbon from the carbon dioxide in the early atmosphere gradually became locked up as carbonate minerals and fossil fuels in sedimentary rocks.
- The ammonia in the early atmosphere reacted with oxygen to release nitrogen.
- Nitrogen was also produced by living organisms such as denitrifying bacteria.
- As the amount of oxygen increased, an **ozone layer** developed. An ozone molecule consists of three oxygen atoms. This ozone layer filters out harmful ultraviolet radiation from the Sun, enabling new, more complex life forms to develop.

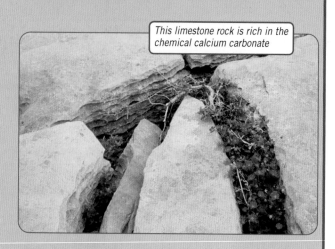

This limestone rock is rich in the chemical calcium carbonate

Is burning fossil fuels going to cause problems?

The level of carbon dioxide in our atmosphere has increased since the Industrial Revolution as we have burnt more fossil fuels. These fossil fuels had stored carbon dioxide from the Earth's early atmosphere for hundreds of millions of years.

Scientists believe that much of the carbon dioxide that is produced is removed from the atmosphere by the **reaction between carbon dioxide and seawater**.

Scientific process

Our ideas about the evolution of the Earth's atmosphere come from scientists' studies of rocks formed in the past. Our ideas change as more evidence becomes available.

QUICK TEST

❶ Roughly how much of today's atmosphere is made up of oxygen?

❷ What is the main gas in the atmosphere today?

❸ What other gases are present in small amounts in the Earth's atmosphere?

❹ Which gases formed the Earth's early atmosphere?

❺ Which was the main gas in the Earth's early atmosphere?

❻ How did the evolution of plants affect the Earth's atmosphere?

❼ What happened to most of the carbon dioxide in the Earth's early atmosphere?

❽ What does the ozone layer do?

❾ How did the development of the ozone layer affect life on Earth?

❿ Why is the amount of carbon dioxide in the Earth's atmosphere increasing?

Pollution of the atmosphere

The atmosphere can be polluted in many ways.

Acid rain

Fossil fuels like coal, oil and gas often contain small amounts of **sulphur**. When these fuels are burnt, the gas **sulphur dioxide**, SO_2 is produced. This gas can dissolve in rainwater to form sulphuric acid and so **acid rain**. Acid rain can affect the environment by damaging statues and buildings, as well as plant and aquatic life.

Carbon monoxide

The gas carbon monoxide can also cause problems. When fossil fuels containing carbon and hydrogen are burnt, the gases carbon dioxide and water vapour are produced. However, if carbon is burnt in an **insufficient supply of oxygen**, the gas carbon monoxide can also be produced.

Incomplete combustion is undesirable in several ways:

- *Carbon monoxide is produced.*
- *Less heat than expected is given off when the fuel is burnt.*
- *Soot is produced which must then be cleaned (a sooty flame has a yellow colour).*

Global dimming

Global dimming is caused by **smoke particles** that are released into the atmosphere. Scientists believe that these smoke particles reduce the amount of sunlight that reaches the Earth's surface and may even affect weather patterns.

Scientific process

Not all scientists believe that human activity is causing global warming. Other factors, such as solar cycles, may be more important. Until we have more evidence, we will not really know.

Carbon dioxide and the greenhouse effect

The **greenhouse effect** is slowly heating up the Earth. When fossil fuels are burnt, the gas carbon dioxide is produced. Although some of this carbon dioxide is removed from the atmosphere by the reaction between carbon dioxide and seawater, the overall amount of carbon dioxide in the atmosphere has increased over the last two hundred years. The carbon dioxide gas **traps the heat energy** that has reached the Earth from the Sun. Global warming may mean that the polar icecaps will eventually melt and this could cause massive flooding, loss of land and habitats.

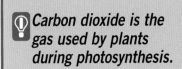 *Carbon dioxide is the gas used by plants during photosynthesis.*

layer of CO_2

heat radiation reflected back to the Earth

light energy from the Sun

Catalytic converters

In this country, modern petrol cars have catalytic converters or 'cats'. The 'cat' is part of the car's exhaust system and helps to **reduce the amount of harmful gases** that the car releases into the atmosphere.

QUICK TEST

1. What is the name of the gas produced when sulphur is burnt?

2. How can switching off lights prevent the formation of acid rain?

3. How can you tell a fuel is being burnt in a poor supply of oxygen?

4. What gas is produced when carbon is burnt in a good supply of oxygen?

5. What gas is produced when carbon is burnt in an insufficient supply of oxygen?

6. What causes global dimming?

7. Which gas is linked to the greenhouse effect?

8. What device is fitted to a car's exhaust system to reduce the levels of harmful pollutants that the car releases into the atmosphere?

Pollution of the environment

All substances are obtained or made from matter from the Earth's crust, sea or atmosphere. It is vital that we protect the environment from harmful pollution.

Problems with nitrate fertilisers

Nitrate fertilisers can cause problems if they are washed into lakes or streams.

- Algae (small plants) thrive in the fertiliser-rich water and grow very well.
- Eventually the algae die and bacteria start to decompose (break down) the algae.
- As the bacteria decompose the algae, they use up all the oxygen in the water.
- Fish and other aquatic life cannot get enough oxygen and so they also die.

This process is called **eutrophication**. Nitrate fertilisers can also find their way into our drinking water supplies. There have been health concerns over the levels of nitrate in water. Although no firm links have yet been proved, it seems wise that the **levels of nitrate in drinking water should be limited** until more is known.

Eutrophication

Problems with bauxite quarrying

Aluminium is used to make drinks cans

Aluminium is extracted from its ore **bauxite**. Unfortunately, this ore is often found in environmentally sensitive areas like the Amazonian **rainforest**. Bauxite is extracted from large opencast mines. Every new mine means that many trees have to be cut down. Trees also have to be cleared when new roads are built to give access to the mines. In addition, the area around the mine can become polluted by litter and oil.

Problems with limestone quarrying

Limestone is a very important raw material. The economic benefits of quarrying for limestone, however, have to be balanced against the social and environmental consequences of quarrying. Limestone has to be blasted from hillsides in huge quantities. This **scars the landscape, causes noise pollution and dust, and affects local wildlife**.

Transporting limestone from the quarry can also cause problems, with **heavy lorries causing noise, congestion and damaging local roads**.

Quarrying, however, does create new **jobs** and brings new **money** into an area.

Problems disposing of plastic

Plastics are very useful materials.

- Plastics are very stable and unreactive.
- Most plastics do not react with water, oxygen or other common chemicals.

- Plastics are also **non-biodegradable**, which means that they are not decomposed by micro-organisms.

However, when plastic objects are no longer needed they do not rot away. They remain in the environment and may cause problems. Plastic objects now fill many landfill sites.

We can get rid of plastics by burning them, but this solution can also cause problems. Although some plastics burn quite easily, they can give off harmful gases. The common plastic, PVC, releases the gas hydrogen chloride when it is burnt.

In response to these problems, scientists have developed new, biodegradable plastics which will eventually rot away.

This plastic bag is 100% degradable* but you can still reuse it!

*From date of manufacture, the plastic will start to degrade in approx.18 months time. The whole process will take about 3 years. See bottom of bag for date of manufacture.

epi

QUICK TEST

1. In what products are nitrate chemicals found?

2. What happens when algae die?

3. Name the main ore of aluminium.

4. Name one place where aluminium ore can be mined from.

5. What is the name used to describe materials that are not broken down by micro-organisms?

6. How can limestone extraction affect the landscape?

Evidence for plate tectonics

Silicon, oxygen and aluminium are all very abundant in the Earth's crust.

Structure of the Earth

Scientists think that the Earth has a layered structure. The crust which we live on is very thin. The next layer down is called the mantle. The mantle is mainly solid, but small amounts must be liquid because the mantle flows very slowly. At the centre of the Earth is the core. The inner core is under great pressure and is solid. The outer core is under slightly less pressure and is liquid.

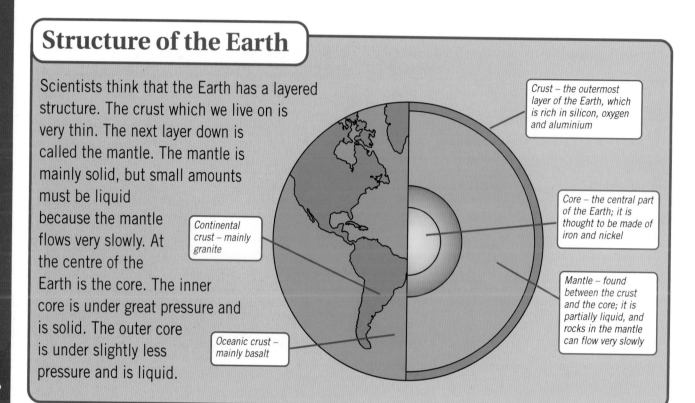

Crust – the outermost layer of the Earth, which is rich in silicon, oxygen and aluminium

Continental crust – mainly granite

Core – the central part of the Earth; it is thought to be made of iron and nickel

Mantle – found between the crust and the core; it is partially liquid, and rocks in the mantle can flow very slowly

Oceanic crust – mainly basalt

Movement of the crust

The ideas involved in plate tectonics were first proposed by the scientist, Alfred Wegener. At first these ideas were resisted, particularly by religious groups, but as more evidence emerged, the theory of plate tectonics was gradually accepted.

The main idea in plate tectonics is that the Earth's **lithosphere** (crust and upper mantle) is split up into about 12 large plates. Each of these plates moves slowly over the Earth's surface at a rate of just a few centimetres a year. The movement of the plates is caused by **convection currents in the mantle**. These currents are created by the **natural radioactive decay** of elements deep inside the Earth which release heat energy.

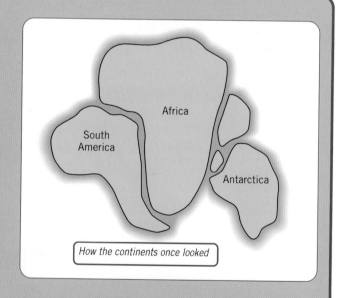

South America

Africa

Antarctica

How the continents once looked

At one time, all the continents were joined together to form a supercontinent called Pangea. Since that time, the continents have moved apart and are now at about their maximum separation.

Clues that support plate tectonics

There are many clues that support our ideas about plate tectonics.

1 As soon as the South American coast was mapped, people began to notice how the east coast of South America and the west coast of Africa fitted together like pieces of an enormous **jigsaw**.

2 Examination of **fossil remains** in South America and Africa showed that rocks of the same age both contained the remains of an unusual freshwater crocodile-type creature.

3 Further evidence that South America and Africa were once joined was found when scientists discovered that **rock strata** of the same age were strikingly similar on both sides of the Atlantic.

4 British rocks that were formed in the Carboniferous period (300 million years ago) must have formed in tropical swamps. Yet rocks found in Britain which formed 200 million years ago must have formed in deserts. This shows that Britain moved through **different climatic zones** as the tectonic plate that Britain rests on moved across the Earth's surface.

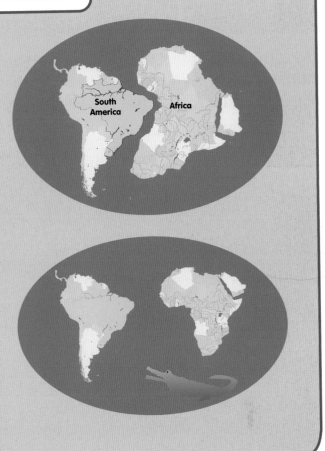

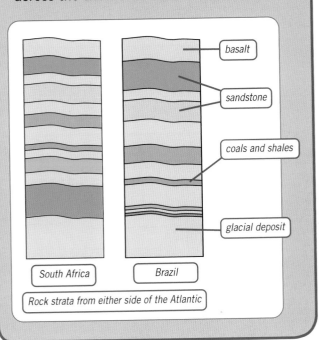

basalt

sandstone

coals and shales

glacial deposit

South Africa

Brazil

Rock strata from either side of the Atlantic

Scientific process

Our ideas about plate tectonics have changed over time. Scientists build a model which fits with the evidence available to them. When new evidence is found, scientists must re-evaluate their existing models and, if necessary, change the model to fit with the new evidence.

QUICK TEST

1. What name is given to the outer layer of the Earth?

2. In which state is the Earth's inner core?

3. Which elements are abundant in the Earth's crust?

4. Which elements are abundant in the Earth's core?

5. How fast do tectonic plates move?

6. What is the Earth's lithosphere?

Consequences of plate tectonics

The movement of tectonic plates can cause many problems, including earthquakes and volcanoes. These problems tend to be worse near the edges of plates. These are known as the plate boundaries.

Earthquakes

Earthquakes are caused by tectonic plates sliding past each other.

The San Andreas Fault, in California, is a famous example of where this is occurring. In fact, the plates in this area have been fractured into a very complicated pattern. As the plates try to move past each other, they tend to stick together rather than smoothly slide past. When the plates stick together, forces build up, until eventually, the **plates move suddenly**. The strain that has built up is released as an earthquake. If this happens under the oceans, catastrophic tsunami waves can result.

Scientists have studied earthquakes to try and be able to predict exactly when they might happen. However, with so many factors involved, it is not always possible to predict exactly when an earthquake will occur.

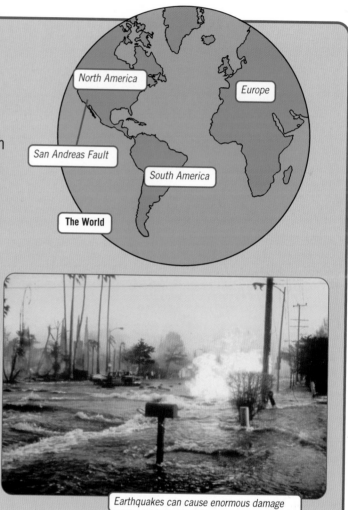

North America

Europe

San Andreas Fault

South America

The World

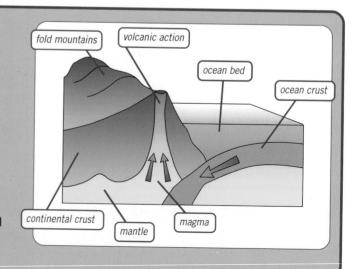

Earthquakes can cause enormous damage

Volcanoes

Volcanoes are found in locations around the Earth where two plates are moving towards each other.

- These convergent plate boundaries often involve the collision between an oceanic and a continental plate.
- **Oceanic plates** contain minerals which are rich in the elements iron and magnesium and are denser than continental plates.

fold mountains

volcanic action

ocean bed

ocean crust

continental crust

mantle

magma

Plate boundaries

- When an oceanic plate and a continental plate converge, the denser, oceanic plate is forced beneath the continental plate.
- The continental plate is stressed and the existing rocks are folded and metamorphosed.
- As the oceanic plate is forced down below the continental plate, seawater lowers the melting point of the rock and some of the oceanic plate may melt to form **magma**. This magma may rise up through cracks to form volcanoes.
- As the plates are moving past each other, earthquakes are also common in these areas.

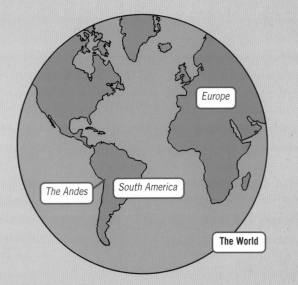

- A convergent plate boundary along the western coast of South America has caused the Andes mountain range.

Mid-ocean ridge basalts

Another consequence of plate tectonics is the formation of mid-ocean ridge basalts.

When tectonic plates move apart, magma comes to the surface. This normally occurs under oceans. As the molten rock cools, it solidifies and forms the igneous rock **basalt**. In fact, these plate boundaries are often referred to as constructive plate boundaries because new crust is being made. Basalt is rich in iron which is magnetic. As the basalt cools down, the iron rich minerals in the basalt line up with the Earth's magnetic field.

By examining the direction in which these minerals have lined up, scientists are able to work out the direction of the Earth's magnetic field. However, examination of the basalt rocks on either side of a mid-ocean ridge shows a striped magnetic reversal pattern. The pattern is symmetrical about the ridge and is evidence that periodically the Earth's magnetic field changes direction. This reversal appears to be very sudden and to occur about every half a million years.

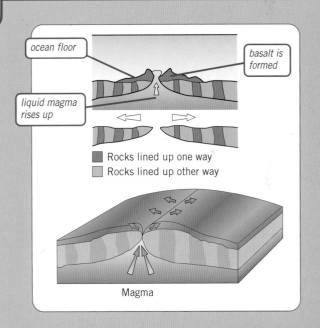

According to the rock record, we are now well overdue another reversal!

QUICK TEST

1. How are earthquakes caused?
2. Why can't scientists predict the exact date of an earthquake?
3. Where is the San Andreas Fault?
4. Which type of plate is densest?

Extraction of iron

Iron is an element. Elements are substances which are made of only one type of atom. There are only about one hundred different elements.

Iron is an extremely important metal. It is extracted from iron ore in the blast furnace.

Methods of extraction

- The more reactive a metal is, the harder it is to remove it from its compound.
- Gold is so unreactive that it is found uncombined.
- However, all other metals are found in compounds. Occasionally we may find rocks that contain metals in such high concentrations that it is economically worthwhile to extract the metal from the rock. Such rocks are called **ores**.
- The exact method chosen to extract the metal depends on the reactivity of the metal.

Iron is less reactive than carbon. Iron can be extracted from iron oxide by reducing the metal oxide with carbon.

potassium	
sodium	**metals that are more**
calcium	**reactive than carbon**
magnesium	**are extracted by**
aluminium	**electrolysis**

carbon	
zinc	**metals that are less**
iron	**reactive than carbon**
tin	**are extracted by**
lead	**reducing the metal**
gold	**oxide using carbon**
	(or carbon monoxide)

The solid raw materials

The solid raw materials in the blast furnace are:

- iron ore
- coke (which is a source of the element carbon)
- limestone (which reacts with impurities).

The main ore of iron is **haematite**. This ore contains the compound iron (III) oxide.

What happens in the blast furnace? 1

1 First hot air is blasted into the furnace. The oxygen in the air reacts with the carbon in the coke to form carbon dioxide and release energy.

> carbon + oxygen → carbon dioxide

2 At the very high temperatures inside the blast furnace, carbon dioxide reacts with more carbon to form carbon monoxide.

> carbon dioxide + carbon → carbon monoxide

What happens in the blast furnace? 2

3 The carbon monoxide reacts with iron oxide to form iron and carbon dioxide.

iron oxide	+	carbon monoxide	→	iron	+	carbon dioxide

During this reaction:

- the iron oxide is reduced to iron
- the carbon monoxide is oxidised to carbon dioxide.

Due to the high temperatures in the blast furnace, the iron that is made is a liquid. This molten iron is dense and sinks to the bottom of the furnace where it can be removed.

Iron ore is mainly reduced by the gas carbon monoxide.

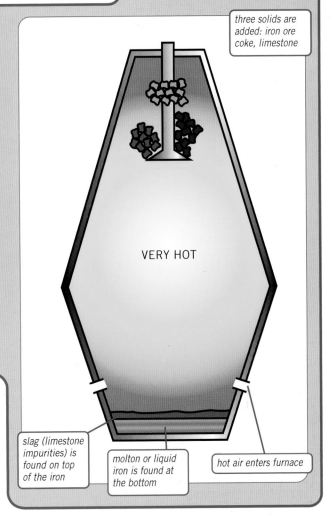

three solids are added: iron ore coke, limestone

VERY HOT

slag (limestone impurities) is found on top of the iron

molton or liquid iron is found at the bottom

hot air enters furnace

Removing impurities in the blast furnace

Haematite (iron ore) contains many impurities; most commonly it contains substantial amounts of silicon dioxide (silica). Limestone is added to the blast furnace because it reacts with these silica impurities to form **slag**. Slag has a low density so floats to the top of the iron ore where it can be removed. The slag can be used in road building and in the manufacture of fertilisers.

❶ Which element is so unreactive that it can be found uncombined?

❷ Which method of extraction can be used for metals that are less reactive than carbon?

❸ Which method of extraction can be used for metals that are more reactive than carbon?

❹ What is the name of the main ore of iron?

❺ What are the three solid raw materials added to the blast furnace?

❻ What is the other raw material used in the blast furnace?

❼ Which gas actually reduces iron oxide to iron?

❽ Why does iron sink to the bottom of the furnace?

❾ What is the name of the substance formed when limestone reacts with silica?

❿ How can this substance be used?

Iron and steel

Most of the iron made in the blast furnace is used to produce steel.

Preventing iron rusting

Iron corrodes or 'rusts' faster than most transition metals. However, rusting requires the presence of both oxygen and water.

Coating the iron
Painting or coating iron in plastic or oil can stop oxygen and water from reaching the metal and prevent it rusting.

Sacrificial protection
We can stop iron from rusting by placing it in contact with a more reactive metal, like zinc or magnesium. The iron is protected because the more reactive metal reacts instead of the iron. Expensive objects made from iron, such as speedboat engines, are protected in this way.

Alloying the metal
Iron can also be protected by mixing the metal with other metals and carbon to form alloys such as **stainless steel**.

Cast iron

The iron that is made in the blast furnace contains quite large amounts of the element carbon. If this iron is allowed to cool down and solidify, it forms cast iron. Cast iron contains about 96% pure iron. This metal can be used to make objects like drain covers. Cast iron:

- is hard
- is strong
- does not rust.

Cast iron does have one notable disadvantage: it is brittle and can easily crack.

Drain covers need to be strong and must not rust. They are made from cast iron

Wrought iron

Wrought iron is made by removing the impurities from cast iron. It is much softer than cast iron and can be used to make objects like gates.

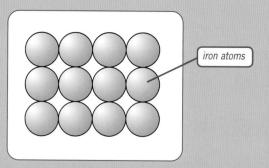

iron atoms

Wrought iron is softer than cast iron because of its structure. Wrought iron is made from almost pure iron. This means that the iron atoms form a very regular arrangement. The layers of iron atoms are able to slip easily over each other. This makes wrought iron soft and easy to shape.

Steel

Most iron is made into steel.

- First, the carbon impurities are removed from iron to produce pure iron.
- Next, other metals and carefully controlled amounts of the non-metal element carbon are added to the iron.

Steel is much harder than wrought iron because it consists of atoms of different elements. These atoms are different sizes. This means that the atoms in steel cannot pack together to form a regular structure. This irregular structure makes it very difficult for layers of atoms to slide over each other and makes steel hard.

Designer steels

By carefully controlling the amount of carbon that is added to steel, scientists can produce steel which has exactly the right properties for each particular job.

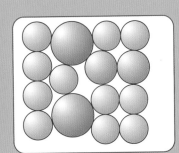

Low carbon steels are:

- soft
- easy to shape.

Objects such as car bodies are made from low carbon steels.

Medium carbon steels are:

- harder
- stronger
- less easy to shape.

Objects such as hammers are made from medium carbon steels.

High carbon steels are:

- hard
- strong
- brittle
- hard to shape.

Objects such as razor blades are made from high carbon steels.

We can also alloy iron with other metals to form different types of steel.

Stainless steel

Stainless steel is a very widely used **alloy**. It consists of:

- 70% iron
- 20% chromium
- 10% nickel.

Stainless steel is extremely resistant to corrosion.

QUICK TEST

QUICK TEST

1. What is the main use of iron?
2. What must be present for iron to rust?
3. How does oiling an iron object stop it from rusting?
4. Name a metal which could be used in sacrificial protection to stop iron rusting.
5. What is the main impurity in cast iron?
6. Give four properties of cast iron.
7. What is the name given to very pure iron?
8. Why is pure iron soft?
9. Which non-metal element is used to make steel?
10. Which metals can be alloyed to form stainless steel?

Aluminium

Aluminium is very abundant in the Earth's crust, but it is also very reactive. This makes it hard to extract. Consequently, aluminium is more expensive than iron.

The main ore of aluminium is called *bauxite*. Bauxite contains the compound aluminium oxide, Al_2O_3.

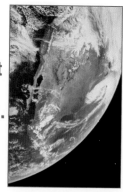

Aluminium alloys are strong and lightweight

Recycling aluminium

Recycling has many advantages:

- we will not have to extract so much bauxite
- landfill sites will not be filled up with discarded aluminium cans

- recycling aluminium uses much less energy than extracting aluminium straight from its ore.

Properties of aluminium

Although pure aluminium is quite soft, when it is alloyed with other metals it becomes much stronger. Aluminium alloys combine high strength with low density. This makes aluminium a very useful metal for making objects like aeroplanes and mountain bikes.

Aluminium is quite a reactive metal and yet it is widely used to make drinks cans. In fact, aluminium appears to be much less reactive than its position in the reactivity series suggests. This is because when aluminium objects are made, their surfaces quickly react with oxygen to form a thin layer of

aluminium oxide. This layer stops the aluminium metal from coming into contact with other chemicals and so prevents any further reaction. The layer of aluminium oxide means that it is quite safe for us to drink fizzy, acidic drinks from aluminium cans.

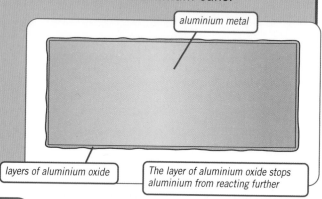

aluminium metal

layers of aluminium oxide

The layer of aluminium oxide stops aluminium from reacting further

The extraction of aluminium

Aluminium is more reactive than carbon so it is extracted using electrolysis, even though this is a very expensive method. The main ore of aluminium is bauxite, which contains aluminium oxide. For electrolysis to occur, the aluminium ions and oxide ions in bauxite must be able to move. This means that the bauxite has to be either heated until it melts or dissolved in something.

Bauxite has a very high melting point and heating the ore to this temperature is very expensive. Fortunately, another ore of aluminium called **cryolite** has a much lower melting point. First the cryolite is heated up until it melts and then the bauxite is dissolved in the molten cryolite.

Electrolysis

Aluminium can now be extracted by electrolysis (using electricity).

1 By dissolving the aluminium oxide, both the aluminium, Al^{3+} and the oxide, O^{2-} ions can move.

2 During electrolysis the aluminium, Al^{3+} ions are attracted to the negative electrode where they pick up electrons to form aluminium, Al atoms. The aluminium metal collects at the bottom of the cell where it can be collected.

> aluminium ions + electrons → aluminium atoms

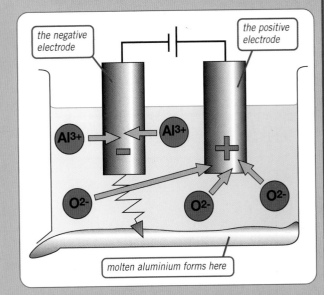

the negative electrode

the positive electrode

Al^{3+} Al^{3+}

O^{2-} O^{2-} O^{2-}

molten aluminium forms here

3 The oxide, O^{2-} ions are attracted to the positive electrode where they deposit electrons to form oxygen molecules.

> oxide ions – electrons → oxygen molecules

4 The oxygen that forms at the positive electrode readily reacts with the **carbon, graphite electrode** to form carbon dioxide. This means the electrodes, must be replaced periodically.

Oxidation and reduction

In the electrolysis of aluminium oxide:

- aluminium ions are reduced to aluminium atoms
- oxide ions are oxidised to oxygen molecules.

Reduction and oxidation reactions must always occur together and so are sometimes referred to as **redox** reactions.

QUICK TEST

1 Name the main ore of aluminium.

2 Give two properties of pure aluminium.

3 What is a mixture of metals called?

4 Why is aluminium less reactive than expected?

5 What is the formula of aluminium oxide?

6 What is the name of the method used to extract aluminium from its ore?

7 During the electrolysis of aluminium oxide which ions are oxidised?

8 During the electrolysis of aluminium oxide which ions are reduced?

9 What are the electrodes made from?

10 Why should the electrodes be periodically replaced?

Titanium

Despite being very abundant in the Earth's crust, *titanium* is an expensive metal. This is because it is difficult to extract titanium from its ore.

The F22 fighter is made from a titanium alloy

Properties of titanium

Titanium has some very special properties. Titanium:

- is very strong when alloyed with other metals
- has a very low density
- is easy to shape
- has a very high melting point
- is very resistant to corrosion.

Titanium appears to be unreactive because the surface of titanium objects quickly reacts with oxygen to form a layer of **titanium oxide**. This layer prevents any further reaction taking place.

Uses of titanium

Titanium's properties mean that this metal is very useful. Titanium alloys are used to make:

- replacement hip and elbow joints
- aircraft
- rockets and missiles.

Titanium ore

The main ore of titanium is **rutile**. Rutile contains the compound titanium dioxide, TiO_2. Rutile is a very hard mineral which is resistant to weathering and is found mixed among sand on certain beaches.

Extraction of titanium

Titanium is more reactive than carbon so it cannot be extracted simply by heating titanium dioxide with carbon. In fact, the extraction of titanium is quite a complicated process.

- First the titanium dioxide is converted to **titanium chloride**.
- Next the titanium chloride is reacted with **molten magnesium**. Magnesium is more reactive than titanium and a chemical reaction takes place in which titanium is displaced.

> titanium chloride + magnesium → titanium + magnesium chloride

This reaction is carried out under a vacuum to stop the titanium from reacting with oxygen in air to form titanium dioxide.

Smart alloys 1

Smart alloys are new materials with amazing properties. One famous example of a smart alloy is **Nitinol**. This is an alloy of nickel and titanium. Smart alloys have a shape memory. When a force is applied to a smart alloy, it stretches. But when a smart alloy is heated up, it returns to its original shape.

Why do smart alloys have a shape memory?

Smart alloys appear to have a shape memory because they are able to exist in two solid forms. A temperature change of 10–20°C is enough to cause smart alloys to change forms.

In smart alloys, the low temperature form and the high temperature form are the same shape and size, so when they are heated smart alloys appear to have a shape memory.

Smart alloys 2

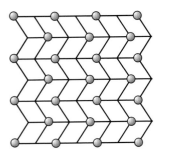

At low temperatures, smart alloys exist in their low temperature form

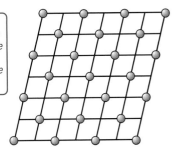

If a force is applied to the alloy it can be deformed to form the low temperature, deformed form of the alloy

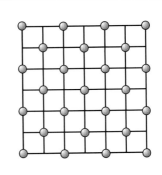

When the alloy is heated, it changes to the higher temperature form

Nano-materials

Scientists are currently researching the properties of new **nano-materials**. These substances contain just a few hundred atoms and vary in size from 1 nm to 100 nm. They have a very high surface area to volume ratio.

Scientists hope that this will allow them to use nano-molecules in exciting ways such as:

- in new computers
- as better catalysts.

QUICK TEST

❶ How can titanium be made stronger?

❷ Why does titanium appear to be unreactive?

❸ How is titanium used inside the human body?

❹ What is the main ore of titanium?

❺ What is the chemical name of the main ore of titanium?

❻ Where is titanium ore collected from?

❼ Why is titanium not extracted from its ore by using carbon?

❽ Which metal is more reactive: titanium or magnesium?

❾ Give the word equation for the reaction between titanium chloride and magnesium.

❿ Which metals are used to produce the smart alloy nitinol?

Copper

Copper is an unreactive metal that has been known since ancient times.

Properties of copper

This saucepan is made from copper. Copper is a good thermal conductor and does not contaminate the food that is being cooked

Copper has some very special properties. Copper is:

- a good thermal conductor
- a good electrical conductor
- easy to shape
- very unreactive
- very resistant to corrosion.

In fact, copper metal is so unreactive that it doesn't even react with water.

Uses of copper

Copper's properties mean that it is a very useful metal. Copper is used to make:

- water pipes
- saucepans
- electrical wires.

Copper ore

The most important ores of copper are **chalcopyrite** and **chalcosine**.

Extraction of copper

Copper is extracted from its ores using the following steps:

1 The **copper sulphide is heated in air to form copper oxide and sulphur dioxide.**

> copper sulphide + oxygen → copper oxide + sulphur dioxide

2 Then the **copper oxide is reacted with more copper sulphide to form copper and sulphur dioxide.**

> copper oxide + copper sulphide → copper + sulphur dioxide

Copper can be extracted from its ore chalcopyrite

The copper produced in this way is not pure enough for many uses.

Purification of copper 1

Copper has to be purified before it can be used for certain applications such as in high specification wiring. Copper is purified using electrolysis.

Electrolysis involves passing an electrical current through a molten ionic substance or dissolved ionic substance to break down the substance into simpler parts.

Purification of copper 2

- During the electrolysis of copper, the impure copper metal is used as the positive electrode.
- At the positive electrode, the copper atoms give up electrons to form copper ions.
- As the positive electrode dissolves away,

| copper atoms − electrons → copper ions |

any impurities fall to the bottom of the cell to form sludge.
- Copper ions in the solution are attracted towards the negative electrode.
- At the negative electrode, the copper ions gain electrons to form copper atoms.

| copper ions + electrons → copper atoms |

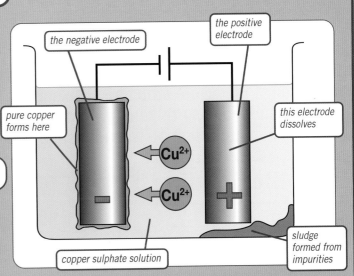

the negative electrode

the positive electrode

pure copper forms here

Cu^{2+}

Cu^{2+}

this electrode dissolves

sludge formed from impurities

copper sulphate solution

- Overall, the positive electrode gets smaller while the negative electrode gets bigger. In addition, the negative electrode is covered in very pure copper.

Copper alloys

Pure copper is too soft for many uses. In pure copper, the atoms are all the same size so they form a regular arrangement. Copper is soft because layers of atoms can pass easily over each other.

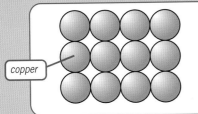

copper

Copper is often mixed with other metals to form alloys.

Bronze is made by mixing copper and tin. It is much harder than either copper or tin. Bronze consists of different-sized atoms, which means that the atoms cannot pack together to form a regular structure.

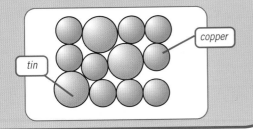

tin

copper

Bronze is hard because the layers of atoms cannot pass easily over each other. Historically, the invention of bronze was a major advance; it was used to make new, stronger tools and weapons. **Brass is made by mixing copper and zinc**.

QUICK TEST

1. Name two copper ores.
2. What is the gas produced when copper sulphide is heated in air?
3. What method is used to purify copper?
4. What is a mixture of metals called?
5. Give the word equation for the reaction which takes place at the negative electrode during the purification of copper.
6. If you wanted to coat a metal object with copper, which electrode should you attach it to?
7. Which metals are used to make bronze?
8. Which metals are used to make brass?

Transition metals

Metals have a giant structure. In metals, the electrons in the highest energy shells (outer electrons) are not bound to one atom, but are free to move through the whole structure. This means that metals consist of positive metals ions surrounded by a sea of negative electrons. Metallic bonding is the attraction between these ions and the electrons.

Metallic bonding

Metallic bonding means that metals have several very useful properties.

- The free electrons mean that metals are **good electrical conductors**.
- The free electrons also mean that metals are **good thermal conductors**.

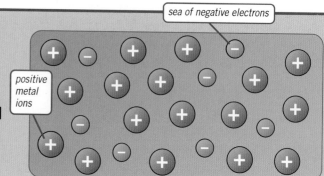

sea of negative electrons

positive metal ions

Group	1	2											3	4	5	6	7	0
Period																		
1								He 1										He 2
2	Li 3	Be 4											B 5	C 6	N 7	O 8	F 9	Ne 10
3	Na 11	Mg 12											Al 13	Si 14	P 15	S 16	Cl 17	Ar 18
4	K 19	Ca 20	Sc 21	Ti 22	V 23	Cr 24	Mn 25	Fe 26	Co 27	Ni 28	Cu 29	Zn 30	Ga 31	Ge 32	As 33	Se 34	Br 35	Kr 36
5	Rb 37	Sr 38	Y 39	Zr 40	Nb 41	Mo 42	Tc 43	Ru 44	Rh 45	Pd 46	Ag 47	Cd 48	In 49	Sn 50	Sb 51	Te 52	I 53	Xe 54
6	Cs 55	Ba 56	57– 71*	Hf 72	Ta 73	W 74	Re 75	Os 76	Ir 77	Pt 78	Au 79	Hg 80	Tl 81	Pb 82	Bi 83	Po 84	At 85	Rn 86
7	Fr 87	Ra 88	89– 103**															

- The strong attraction between the metal ions and the electrons means that metals can be drawn into **wires** as the ions slide over each other.
- Metals can also be **hammered into shape**.

Properties of metals 1

The transition metals are found in the middle section of the periodic table. Copper, iron and nickel are examples of very useful transition metals. All transition metals have characteristic properties.

They:

- have **high melting points** (except for mercury which is a liquid at room temperature)
- have **high densities**
- form coloured compounds.

They are also strong, tough and hard wearing. All transition metals are much less reactive than Group 1 metals. They all react much less vigorously with oxygen and water.

Properties of metals 2

Many transition metals can **form ions with different charges**. This makes transition metals useful catalysts in many reactions.

Transition metals all have similar properties because of their electron structure. If we consider the first row of the transition elements (scandium to zinc), they all behave in a very similar way. This is because we are actually filling a lower energy electron shell and not the outer electron shell, which determines how the atoms react.

Normally, the third shell can hold up to eight electrons. However, once two electrons have been placed into the fourth shell, this changes and the third shell can hold up to 18 electrons. The outer shell contains two electrons, so the transition metals behave in a similar way to each other.

Copper
- Copper is a good electrical and thermal conductor.
- It can be easily bent into new shapes and does not corrode.
- Copper is widely used in electrical wiring.
- It is also used to make water pipes.

Iron
- Iron made in the blast furnace is strong, but brittle.
- Iron is often made into steel.
- Steel is strong and cheap, and is used in vast quantities. However, it is also heavy and may rust.
- Iron and steel are useful structural materials. They are used to make buildings, bridges, ships, cars and trains.
- Iron is used as a catalyst in the Haber process.

Nickel
- Nickel is hard, shiny and dense.
- It is widely used to make coins.
- Nickel is used as a catalyst in the manufacture of margarine.

Metal alloys

Alloys are made by mixing metals together. In fact, occasionally, alloys can even be made by mixing metals with non-metals.

Common alloys include:

- amalgams, which are mainly mercury
- brass, which is made from copper and zinc
- bronze, which is made from copper and tin
- solder, which is made from lead and tin
- steel, which is mainly iron.

QUICK TEST

1. Why are metals able to conduct heat and electricity?
2. In which part of the periodic table are the transition metals found?
3. What are the characteristics of transition metals?
4. Why is copper used for electrical wiring?
5. Why is copper used for water pipes?
6. Why is iron made into steel?
7. Which items can be made from steel?

Noble gases

The characteristics of noble gases are as follows:

- The noble gases are found on the far right-hand side of the periodic table.
- The noble gases are all colourless.
- They are monatomic gases – this means that they exist as single atoms rather than as diatomic molecules as other gases do.

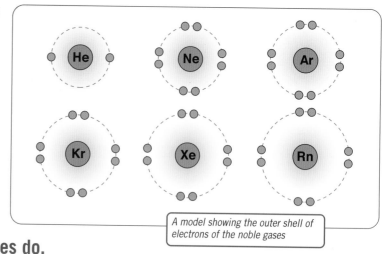

A model showing the outer shell of electrons of the noble gases

Melting points

Why do melting and boiling points increase down the group?

- Down the group, the atoms get larger and have more electrons.
- This means that the strength of the attraction between atoms increases.
- The **forces of attraction between atoms get stronger** down the group, so it takes more energy to overcome these forces. This means the heavier noble gases will melt and boil at higher temperatures.

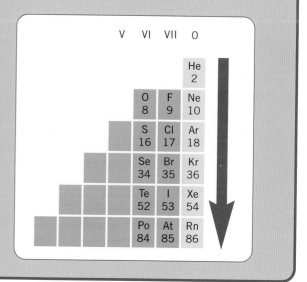

Why are noble gases so unreactive?

- When atoms react they share, gain or lose electrons to obtain a full outer shell of electrons.
- **Noble gases already have a full and stable outer shell so they do not react**.
- However, noble gases are useful precisely because they do not react.
- They are inert which means unreactive.

Radon is a noble gas. It is chemically unreactive but it is radioactive. Home owners in some parts of the country such as Cornwall and Northamptonshire use these devices to monitor radon levels

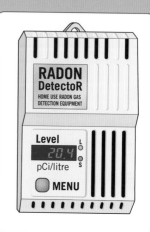

Uses of the noble gases

Helium

- Helium is used in balloons and in airships.
- It is less dense than air.
- It is not flammable (early airships used hydrogen, which is flammable, and this caused problems).

Neon

Neon is used in electrical discharge tubes in advertising signs.

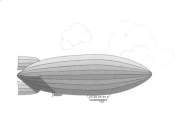

Argon

- Argon is used in filament light bulbs.
- The hot filament is surrounded by argon. This stops the filament from burning away, which would break the bulb.

Krypton

Krypton is used in lasers.

We used to believe that noble gas compounds could never exist. Today a few compounds have been made but they are very unstable.

QUICK TEST

1. Why are the noble gases so unreactive?
2. What is the trend in boiling points down the group?
3. Draw the (outer shell) electron shell of helium.
4. Draw the (outer shell) electron shell of argon.
5. What does monatomic mean?
6. What is helium used for?
7. Why is it used?
8. What is neon used for?
9. What is argon used for?
10. What is krypton used for?

Chemical tests

In this subject, we often wish to identify the chemical present.

Gas tests

Carbon dioxide

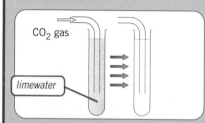

What do you do?
The gas is bubbled through limewater.

What happens?
The limewater turns cloudy.

- Carbonates react with acids to produce **carbon dioxide**.

Chlorine

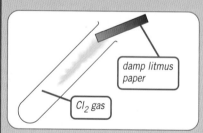

What do you do?
Place damp litmus paper in the gas.

What happens?
The litmus paper is bleached.

Hydrogen

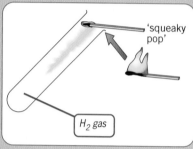

What do you do?
A lighted splint is placed nearby.

What happens?
The hydrogen burns with a squeaky pop.

Oxygen

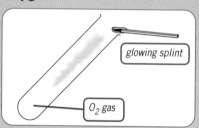

What do you do?
A glowing splint is placed in the gas.

What happens?
The splint relights.

Ammonia

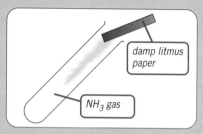

What do you do?
Place damp red litmus paper in the gas.

What happens?
The red litmus paper turns blue.

- Sodium hydroxide solution reacts with ammonium ions to form ammonia.
- Nitrate ions are reduced by aluminium powder and sodium hydroxide to form ammonia.

Testing for alkenes

Alkenes are unsaturated hydrocarbons.

What do you do?
Add bromine water.

What happens?
The orange-brown bromine water becomes colourless.

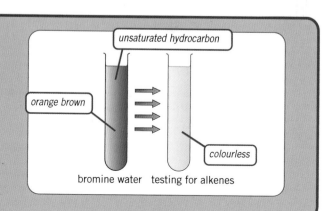

Flame tests

Flame tests can be used to identify some metals present in salts.

What do you do?
1 Clean a flame test wire by placing it into the hottest part of a Bunsen flame.
2 Dip the end of the wire into water and then into the salt sample.
3 Hold the salt into the hottest part of the flame and observe the colour seen.

What happens?
The flame alters according to the salt:

- lithium – red
- potassium – lilac
- barium – apple green.
- sodium – orange
- calcium – brick red

Hydroxide tests

We can identify other metals by adding sodium hydroxide solution to solutions of metal salts. If the unknown metal forms an **insoluble precipitate**, we can use the colour of the precipitate to identify the metal present:

- aluminium – white precipitate which dissolves in excess sodium hydroxide
- calcium – white precipitate
- magnesium – white precipitate
- copper (II) – pale blue precipitate
- iron (II) – green precipitate
- iron (III) – brown precipitate.

Modern instrumental methods

Modern instrumental methods can be used to **detect and identify chemicals**. These modern techniques have many advantages, they are:

- accurate
- sensitive
- fast
- can be used when there are only very small samples available.

Some techniques, such as atomic absorption spectroscopy, are used to identify elements.

Other techniques are used to identify compounds. These include:

- infrared spectroscopy
- ultraviolet spectroscopy
- nuclear magnetic spectroscopy
- gas–liquid chromatography.

Mass spectroscopy can be used to identify elements or compounds.

QUICK TEST

❶ What is the test for carbon dioxide?

❷ What is the test for chlorine?

❸ What is the test for ammonia?

❹ What is the test for unsaturated hydrocarbons?

❺ During a flame test what colour is given by a potassium salt?

❻ During a flame test, what colour is given by a barium salt?

❼ What colour precipitate is formed when a solution of a magnesium salt reacts with sodium hydroxide?

❽ What colour precipitate is formed when a solution of a copper (II) salt reacts with sodium hydroxide?

Practice questions

Use the questions to test your progress. Check your answers on page 125.

1. The table is about limestone and some of the substances that can be made from limestone.

Substance	Information about the substance
A	is made when limestone is heated with silica and soda
B	is made when water is added to calcium oxide
C	is a rock that contains large amounts of calcium carbonate
D	is formed when calcium carbonate is heated

a) What is the name of substance C? ....

b) What is the chemical name of substance D? ....

c) What is the name of substance B? ....

d) What is the name of substance A? ....

2. Atoms can join together to form molecules. Here are four diagrams of molecules.

a) $H-\overset{\overset{\displaystyle H}{|}}{\underset{\underset{\displaystyle H}{|}}{C}}-H$ b) $H-\overset{\overset{\displaystyle H}{|}}{\underset{\underset{\displaystyle H}{|}}{C}}-\overset{\overset{\displaystyle H}{|}}{\underset{\underset{\displaystyle H}{|}}{C}}-H$ c) $\overset{H}{\underset{H}{>}}C=C\overset{H}{\underset{H}{<}}$ d) $H-\overset{\overset{\displaystyle H}{|}}{\underset{\underset{\displaystyle H}{|}}{C}}-\overset{\overset{\displaystyle H}{|}}{C}=C\overset{H}{\underset{H}{<}}$

a) What is the formula of molecule A? ....

b) What is the name of molecule B? ....

c) What family of organic compounds do molecules A and B belong to? ....

d) What is the formula of molecule C? ....

e) What is the name of molecule D? ....

f) What family of organic compounds do molecules C and D belong to? ....

3. Crude oil can be separated into fractions.

a) What is the name of the process used to separate crude oil into fractions? ....

b) Molecules found in the diesel oil fraction contain about 20 carbon atoms, while molecules in the petrol fraction have about 8 carbon atoms.
   Tick one box to show how petrol and diesel molecules compare.
   Compared with diesel molecules, petrol molecules are:

   ☐ more flammable   ☐ more viscous   ☐ have a higher boiling point
   ☐ have more carbon atoms

c) Some long hydrocarbon molecules can be split into smaller, more useful molecules. What is the name of the process used to break up long hydrocarbon molecules into shorter more useful hydrocarbons?

   ....

4. a) What is the name given to a mixture of metals? ....

   ....

   b) Which metals are mixed together to form stainless steel? ....

   ....

   c) Which non-metal element is often added to steel to make it harder? ....

5. a) Sketch the arrangement of atoms in pure titanium. ....

   b) Sketch the arrangement of atoms in a titanium alloy. ....

   c) Explain why titanium alloy is stronger than pure titanium. ....

6. Iron is produced in the blast furnace. Place these statements in order to show how iron is produced.
   a) Carbon dioxide reacts with carbon to form carbon monoxide.
   b) The iron is dense and sinks to the bottom of the furnace where it can be removed.
   c) Carbon reacts with oxygen to form carbon dioxide.
   d) The carbon monoxide reacts with iron oxide to form iron and carbon dioxide.

   ....

7. This table shows the names of four different chemicals.

   a) During a flame test, which chemical produces a red colour?

   ....

Name of chemical
ethene
potassium chloride
lithium chloride
hydrogen

   b) Which substance burns with a squeaky pop?

   ....

   c) Which substance decolourises bromine water?

   ....

   d) During a flame test, which chemical produces a lilac colour?

   ....

8. Atoms can join together to form molecules.
   Here are four diagrams of molecules.

   Molecule A   Molecule B   Molecule C   Molecule D

   a) Which of these diagrams has the formula CH_4? ....

   b) Which of these diagrams has the formula NH_3? ....

   c) Which diagram represents an element? ....

   d) Which diagram is a water molecule? ....

   e) Which diagram is an oxygen molecule? ....

   f) Which diagram is methane? ....

Energy

Many devices take in one kind of energy and change it into another. It is important that we know how well they do this so that we can choose between them and where possible try to improve them.

Different forms of energy

The table below is a reminder of the different forms of energy.

Types of energy	Sources
heat or thermal energy	hot objects such as fires
light energy	the Sun, light bulbs, lamps, etc.
sound energy	loudspeakers, vibrating objects
electrical energy	available every time a current flows
chemical energy	food, fuels and batteries
kinetic energy (the energy an object has because it is moving)	flowing water, wind, etc.
elastic, or strain, potential energy	objects such as springs and rubber bands that are stretched, twisted or bent
gravitational potential energy	objects that have a high position and are able to fall
nuclear energy	reactions in the centre or nucleus of an atom

Energy transfers 1

When energy is used to do something **it does not disappear**. It is **transferred or changed into other, different forms** of energy.

A **light bulb** changes **electrical energy** into **heat and light** energy.

A **loudspeaker** changes **electrical energy** into **sound energy**.

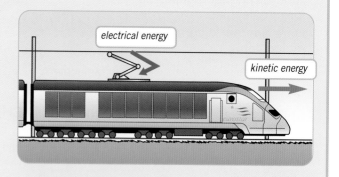

The **motor** inside this train changes **electrical energy** into **kinetic energy**.

Energy transfers 2

Other examples of energy changes are given in the table below.

Energy in	Energy changer	Energy out
chemical	food	heat, kinetic, chemical
light	solar cell	electrical
kinetic	wind turbine	electrical
strain potential energy	bow and arrow	kinetic energy
chemical	battery	electrical
electrical	battery charger	chemical

Efficiency

Usually, when an energy change takes place, only part of the energy is changed into something useful. The remainder is wasted.

Example

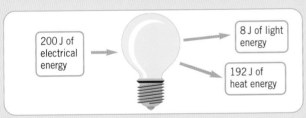

This light bulb is not 100% efficient.
Not all of the energy is changed into light: some of it is changed into heat. To calculate the efficiency of a transfer we use the equation:

$$\text{Efficiency} = \frac{\text{useful energy output}}{\text{total energy input}} \times 100\,\%$$

In this case, 200 J of electrical energy enter the bulb. Of this, 8 J is transferred into light energy and 192 J is transferred into heat.

Using the equation:

$$\text{Efficiency} = \frac{\text{useful energy output}}{\text{total energy input}} \times 100\%$$

The efficiency of the bulb:

$$= \frac{8}{200} \times 100\% = 4\%$$

In nearly all devices, wasted energy is eventually transferred to the surroundings, which then become warmer.

An efficient device saves you money and helps protect the environment by reducing your energy consumption. An inefficient device wastes energy and uses up our energy resources.

QUICK TEST

1. Name five different types of energy.
2. Name three devices that change electrical energy into a different kind of energy.
3. Write down the energy transfer that takes place when someone turns on a hairdryer.
4. Why is it important not to use electrical devices that are inefficient?
5. Calculate the efficiency of a radio that changes 200 J of electrical energy into 180 J of sound energy.

Generating electricity

Electricity is easily converted into other forms of energy and can be transferred across large distances.

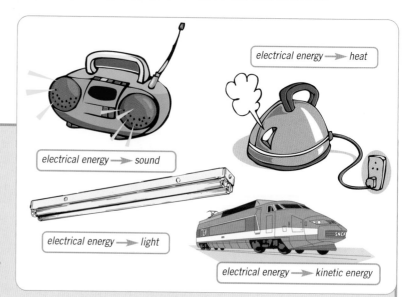

electrical energy → sound

electrical energy → light

electrical energy → heat

electrical energy → kinetic energy

Power stations

Most of the electrical energy we use at home is generated at **power stations**. There are several different types of power station, including those that use **coal, oil or gas as their source of energy (fuel)**.

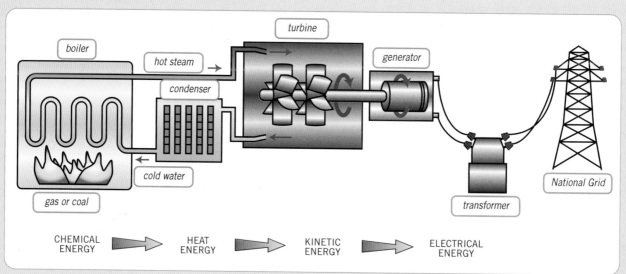

boiler

turbine

hot steam

generator

condenser

cold water

gas or coal

transformer

National Grid

CHEMICAL ENERGY → HEAT ENERGY → KINETIC ENERGY → ELECTRICAL ENERGY

- The fuel is burned to release its **chemical energy**.
- The **heat energy released** is used to heat water and turn it into **steam**.
- The steam **turns turbines**.
- The turbines **turn large generators**.
- The **generators produce electrical energy**.

- Before entering the **National Grid**, the electrical energy passes through a **transformer**, which increases its voltage and decreases the current. These changes **reduce the energy losses in the cables and wires**.
- The electrical energy is then carried to our homes through the National Grid.

Fossil fuels

Coal, oil and gas are called **fossil fuels**. They are **concentrated sources** of energy.

Fossil fuels are formed from **plants and animals** that died over 100 million years ago. When they died they became **covered with many** **layers of mud and earth and changed into fossil fuels**. It takes **millions of years** for these fuels to form. They are called **non-renewable fuels** because once they have been used up they **cannot be replaced**.

The problems with fossil fuels

- When fossil fuels are burned they produce **carbon dioxide**. Increasing the amount of carbon dioxide in the atmosphere will cause the temperature of the Earth and its atmosphere to rise. **This is called the greenhouse effect and could lead to drastic changes in climate, flooding and drought**.
- When coal and oil are burned they also produce gases that cause **acid rain**.

- We are using fossil fuels up very quickly and will soon have to find other sources of energy. It is vital that we start looking for alternative sources of energy now.

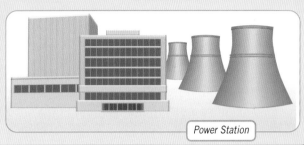

Power Station

The solutions A

First, we need to slow down the rate at which we are using fossil fuels. We can do this by:

- driving smaller cars, using public transport, walking or cycling more.
- developing more efficient car engines.

- **improving the insulation** of our homes and factories so that less energy is wasted heating them.
- turning off lights and turning down heating where possible.

The solutions B

Second, we need to make greater use of **renewable sources of energy** (see page 88).

In the UK, nuclear power stations generate some of our electricity. These stations have the advantage of producing electrical energy without emitting greenhouse or other polluting gases, and the cost of producing electricity is very low. There are, however, several very serious disadvantages that need to be considered:

- The building and decommissioning of nuclear power stations is very expensive.
- Waste nuclear material will remain dangerously radioactive for thousands of years.
- There is always the possibility of leaks into the atmosphere of radioactive materials.
- There is the risk of a nuclear explosion.

We depend upon electricity. Without it our lives would be very different. You should be aware that using as much as we do at present may be damaging our planet. Make sure you understand the problems and know some of the possible solutions.

QUICK TEST

1. Name three fossil fuels.
2. What gas causes the greenhouse effect?
3. Name one type of environmental damage that might be caused as a result of using fossil fuels in our power stations.
4. Why are fossil fuels called non-renewable sources of energy?
5. Suggest three things we could do to make fossil fuels last longer.

Renewable sources of energy

Unlike fossil fuels, there are some sources of energy that will not run out. They are continually being replaced. These are called *renewable sources of energy*. Each of these sources has advantages and disadvantages to their use.

Wind power

The **movement energy (kinetic energy) of the wind** is used to drive turbines and generators.

+ It is a **renewable** source of energy and cannot, therefore, be exhausted.
+ It requires **low level technology** and so can be used by developing countries.
+ It produces **no atmospheric pollution**.
− It produces **visual and noise pollution**.
− It is **limited to windy sites**.
− **With no wind, there can be no energy generated**.

Solar energy

The light energy carried in the Sun's rays can be directly converted into electricity using solar cells.

The heat energy carried in the Sun's rays can also be absorbed by dark coloured panels and used to warm up water.

+ It is a low maintenance option.
+ No pollution from burning fuel.
+ There is no need for power cables.
− It is initially quite expensive.
− It may not be so useful in regions where there is limited sunshine.

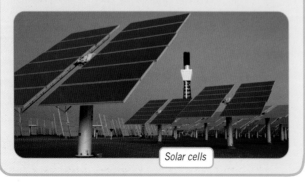

Solar cells

Biomass

The **chemical energy stored in 'things that have grown'**, e.g. wood, can be **released by burning** it. This energy source can be maintained by growing a succession of trees and then cropping them when they mature.

+ It is a **renewable source of energy**.
+ It requires **low level technology** and so can be used by developing countries.
+ It does not add to the greenhouse effect as the carbon dioxide they release when burned was originally taken from the atmosphere as the trees grew.
− **Large areas of land are needed** to grow sufficient numbers of trees.

Geothermal 1

In regions where the Earth's crust is thin, **hot rocks beneath the ground** can be used to heat water, turning it into steam. This steam is then used to drive turbines and generate electricity.

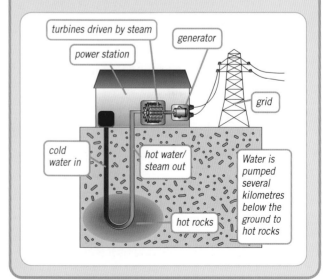

turbines driven by steam

generator

power station

grid

cold water in

hot water/ steam out

Water is pumped several kilometres below the ground to hot rocks

hot rocks

Geothermal 2

- It is a **renewable source of energy**.
- It produces **no pollution and no environmental problems**.
- There are **very few suitable sites**.
- There is a **high cost of drilling** deep into the ground.

Tidal power

At high tide, water is trapped behind a barrage or dam. When it is released at low tide the **gravitational potential energy of the water** changes into **kinetic energy**, which then drives turbines and generates electricity.

- It is a **renewable source of energy**.
- **It is reliable**, with two tides per day.
- It produces **no atmospheric pollution**.
- It has **low running costs**.
- It has a **high initial cost**.
- There is a risk of **possible damage to the environment**, e.g. flooding.

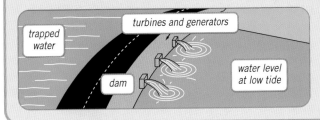

Wave power

The **rocking motion of the waves** is used to generate electricity.

- It is a **renewable source of energy**.
- It produces **no atmospheric pollution**.
- It is **useful for isolated islands**.
- It has a **high initial cost**.
- **It causes visual pollution**.
- **Poor energy capture** - a large area of machines is needed for even a small energy return.

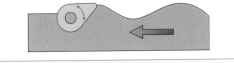

Hydroelectricity

The **kinetic energy of flowing water** is used to drive turbines and generators.

- It is a **renewable source of energy**.
- The energy **can be stored** until required.
- It produces **no atmospheric pollution**.
- **High initial cost**.
- **High cost to environment**, i.e. flooding, loss of habitat.

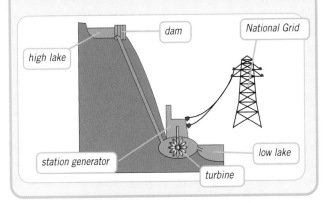

- It is an **obstacle to water transport**.

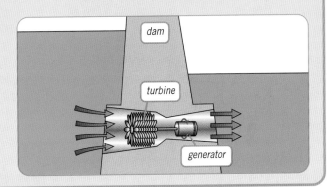

Heat transfer – conduction

Heat will try to move from hot places to cooler places. Sometimes we want this to happen, sometimes we do not. If we understand the different ways in which heat can move, we can take steps to improve this movement or prevent it. Three ways in which heat can move are by: conduction, convection and radiation.

Conduction

Conduction **is the movement of heat by vibrations**.

conduction

The atoms of the rod that are in the fire become hot. They **vibrate more violently**. These vibrations transfer heat to the cooler end of the rod and so it also becomes hot.

After five or ten minutes the whole length of this metal rod is hot. Heat has travelled along the rod by **conduction**.

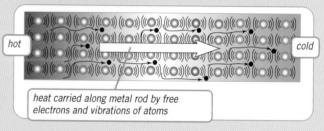

hot   cold

heat carried along metal rod by free electrons and vibrations of atoms

Conductors and insulators 1

All metals are good conductors of heat because the vibrations can be passed along easily. We often use metals to help heat move.

Non-metals, such as plastics, are usually poor conductors of heat. **A poor conductor is called an insulator. Insulators are used to prevent heat from moving.**

Let's have a look at some examples of heat transfer in the home.

Good saucepans are made from **conductors** and **insulators**.

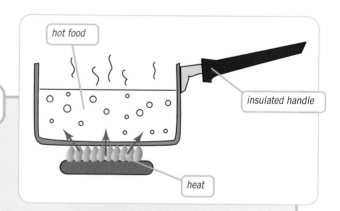

hot food

insulated handle

heat

The base and sides of the pan are made of metal so that heat can pass easily from the flame to the food. The handle is made from an insulator so that it does not become too hot to hold.

Air is an **excellent insulator** and is often used where we want to **prevent heat moving**.

Conductors and insulators 2

Clothes made from wool and cotton contain lots of **trapped air** and so are excellent **insulators.** This is why they keep you warm.

Glass fibre is an excellent insulator because it also contains large amounts of **trapped air**. It is placed in the loft of a house to **stop heat escaping** through the roof.

25% through roof, reduced by putting insulation into loft

10% through windows, reduced by installing double glazing

25% through walls, reduced by having cavity wall insulation

25% through gaps and cracks around doors and windows, reduced by fitting draught excluders

15% through floor, reduced by fitting carpets and underlay

Insulating the home

The diagram above shows how heat may escape from a house that has not been insulated.

Some ways of insulating your home are very cheap and save lots of energy, e.g. loft insulation. Some methods also save lots of energy, but they are expensive to do, e.g. fitting double-glazed windows. When insulating a home, the owner must decide which methods are going to be best.

💡 *Try to remember several uses for conductors and insulators, especially around the home.*

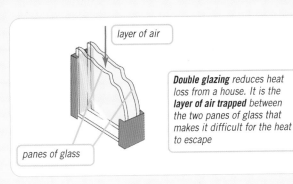

layer of air

panes of glass

Double glazing *reduces heat loss from a house. It is the* **layer of air trapped** *between the two panes of glass that makes it difficult for the heat to escape*

QUICK TEST

① Give one example and one use of a good conductor.

② Give one example and one use of an insulator.

③ Why do woollen hats keep your head warm?

④ What is double glazing?

⑤ Suggest five methods by which you could reduce the heat escaping from your house.

Heat transfer – convection

When air is warmed it rises. If it is allowed to cool it will fall. This movement of air can be used to transfer heat from place to place. It is an example of a convection current.

Rising warm air will lift these balloons into the sky. But what will happen when the air cools?

Heating a room by convection

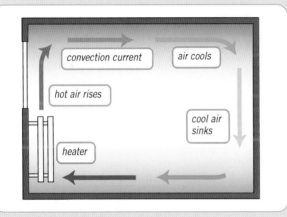

convection current

air cools

hot air rises

cool air sinks

heater

Heat is being carried to all parts of this room by a convection current.

Traditional open fires are not very efficient at warming a room. They create convection currents, which carry a lot of heat up the chimney and then outside.

Convection currents in ovens and fridges

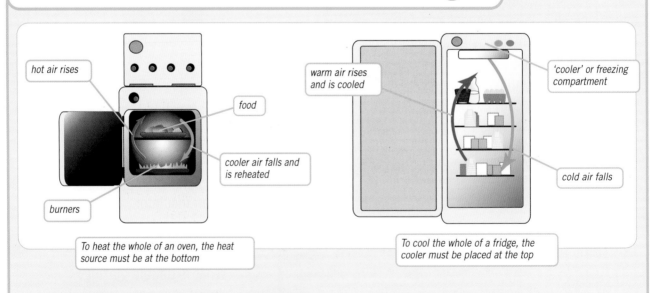

hot air rises

food

cooler air falls and is reheated

burners

warm air rises and is cooled

'cooler' or freezing compartment

cold air falls

To heat the whole of an oven, the heat source must be at the bottom

To cool the whole of a fridge, the cooler must be placed at the top

💡 *It is a common mistake to say that heat rises. It is better to say that warm air rises, carrying heat with it.*

Convection currents in cavity walls

Many older homes have walls that are made up of two layers of bricks with a gap between them. They are called **cavity walls**. The **air gap** between the bricks is a good idea as it stops a lot of heat escaping through the walls by **conduction**. Heat can, however, cross the gap if a convection current is set up.

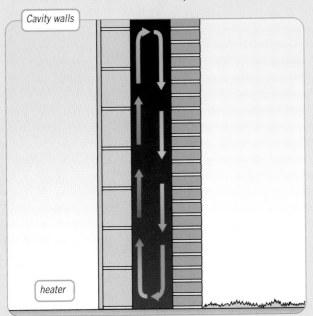

Cavity walls

heater

To prevent this from happening, **foam insulation** can be **injected into the cavity**. The foam contains lots of air but it is **trapped as little bubbles**. It is therefore **unable** to move and form a convection current.

Injecting foam insulation into the cavity

In modern houses, **solid insulation boards** are placed inside the cavity as the house is being built.

Solid insulation boards between two walls

QUICK TEST

1. What happens to air when it is warmed?

2. What happens to air when it cools?

3. Where is the warmest air in a room?

4. Why are traditional open fires inefficient?

5. Why do cavity walls stop some heat escaping from your house?

6. Why should foam be placed inside a cavity wall?

Heat transfer – radiation

Radiation

Radiation is the movement of heat by waves. In the picture below, heat is being carried from the fire to the man's hands by waves. These waves have several different names. They may be called **thermal radiation**, **electromagnetic waves** or **infrared waves**.

All objects give out these waves, even you! They are not very noticeable, however, unless the object is hot. The **hotter** an object, the **more waves it emits**.

The photograph below is called a **thermogram**. It was taken using the radiation given out by the building. The **different colours indicate different temperatures**. The lighter colours are the hottest parts of the building. The coldest parts are shown coloured blue.

Photographs like this are very useful for identifying where heat is being lost from a building

Heat from the Sun

Particles have to be present if heat is moving by **conduction** or **convection**. Heat that is being carried by radiation does not need any particles.

There are no particles between the Sun and the Earth. In this case, how is heat carried from one to the other?

Transfer of heat by radiation

Absorption or reflection

When radiation strikes an object the rays may either be:

■ **absorbed** or
■ **reflected**.

Radiation can be reflected back into a room by placing a sheet of aluminium foil behind the radiator.

*Objects with **dark, rough surfaces** absorb most of the radiation and become warmer*

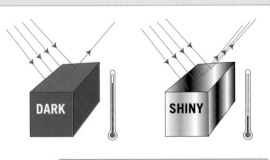

*Objects with **light-coloured, shiny surfaces** reflect most of the radiation and remain cooler*

Solar heater

In hot countries, where fuel is scarce, food can be cooked using a **solar heater** like the one shown on the right.

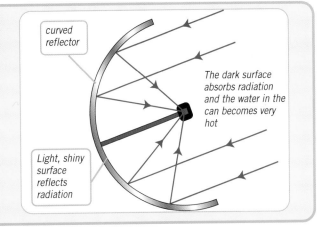

curved reflector

The dark surface absorbs radiation and the water in the can becomes very hot

Light, shiny surface reflects radiation

Emitting radiation

We can sometimes feel the radiation being given off, or emitted, by an object. How do you know a radiator is hot without touching it?

How much radiation an object emits depends upon its **temperature** and its surface.

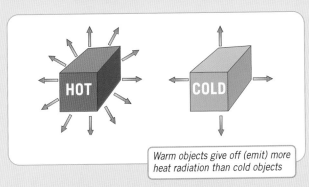

HOT COLD

Warm objects give off (emit) more heat radiation than cold objects

Objects with **dark** or **matt surfaces** give off lots of radiation, i.e. they are **good emitters**. Objects with **light** or **shiny surfaces** give off less radiation, i.e. they are **poor** emitters. This can be proved by this simple experiment with teapots.

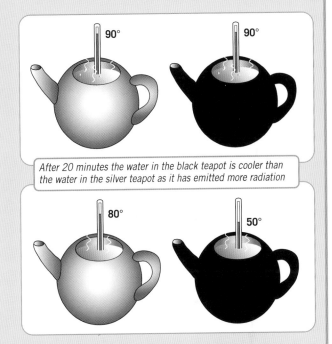

90° 90°

After 20 minutes the water in the black teapot is cooler than the water in the silver teapot as it has emitted more radiation

80° 50°

💡 *Remember, if there are no particles present, radiation is the only way in which heat can move.*

1. What is radiation?
2. Which gives out most radiation, a hot object or a cold one?
3. Why must heat travel from the Sun to Earth by radiation?
4. What two things might happen when radiation strikes an object?
5. What kind of a surface should an object that is a good absorber of radiation have?
6. What kind of a surface should an object that is a poor absorber of radiation have?
7. What is a thermogram?
8. Why will an athlete wrapped in a space blanket keep warm?

Current, charge and resistance

In all electrical circuits we need to control the current flowing.

Charges on the move

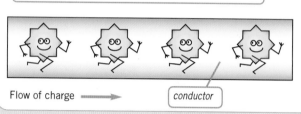

Electricity flows better through conductors than insulators

Flow of charge →

conductor

insulator

I can't move through this!

No (or poor) flow of charge

- An electric current is a **flow of charge**.
- In **metals**, the charges are normally carried around **by electrons**.
- Metals are **good conductors** because they contain lots of electrons that **are able to move around easily**.

- Non-metals are mainly **poor conductors, or insulators**, because **they do not allow charges to move through them easily**.

Making charges move

- **Cells and batteries** act as **charge pumps**, giving the charges **energy**.
- Several cells connected together can give more energy to the charges and produce a larger current in the circuit.
- Several cells connected together are called a **battery**.

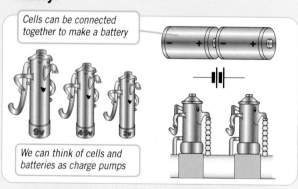

Cells can be connected together to make a battery

We can think of cells and batteries as charge pumps

- The current we get from a cell or battery is called **direct current** or d.c. because it **flows in one direction**.

Some batteries have labels which indicate how much energy they contain, e.g. a 40 amp-hour

battery will deliver a current of 1 A for 40 hours, or a current of 2 A for 20 hours, etc. before it has given up all of its energy.

We **measure current** with an **ammeter**. Current (I) is measured in amps or amperes (A).

Electrical resistance 1

Components in a **circuit resist** current flowing through them. Components called **resistors** are used **to control the size of the current** flowing in a circuit.

If a **variable resistor** is included in a circuit, its value can be altered so that the current flowing in the circuit can easily be changed. When you use a **dimmer switch**, or alter the **volume control** on your TV set, you are using a **variable resistor**.

Electrical resistance 2

Controlling the flow of current using resistors

With no resistors in the circuit, a large current will flow

With a resistor in the circuit, a smaller current will flow

Altering the value of this variable resistor changes the brightness of the bulb

Special resistors

Light dependent resistors (LDRs)
- These have a **high resistance** when there is **little or no light**.
- Their **resistance decreases as light intensity increases**.
- They are used in **light sensitive circuits**, e.g. for controlling **streetlighting** or in **burglar alarms**.

Thermistors
- These are **resistors whose resistance alters greatly as their temperature changes**.

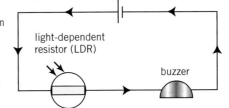

If a burglar turns on the light the resistance of the LDR falls. Current now flows around the circuit and the buzzer sounds

light-dependent resistor (LDR)

buzzer

- The vast majority of these **resistors have resistances** that decrease as their **temperature increases**.
- They are used in **temperature sensitive circuits**, e.g. **fire alarms and thermostats**.

Calculating resistance

The resistance of a component is measured in ohms (Ω) and can be calculated using the equation:

$$R = \frac{V}{I}$$

Example

A current of 3 A flows when a p.d. (potential difference) of 12 V is applied across the wire. Calculate the resistance of the wire.

$$R = \frac{V}{I} = \frac{12\,V}{3\,A} = 4\,\Omega$$

1. What is an electric current?

2. What kind of current does a battery provide?

3. A battery has a label attached to it that says 50 Ah. For approximately how long could you draw a current of 2 A before the battery has given up all its energy?

4. What type of resistor is affected by light? Give one use for this type of resistor.

5. What type of resistor decreases its resistance as its temperature increases? Give one use for this type of resistor.

6. Calculate the resistance of a fixed resistor that has a current of 2 A flowing through it when a p.d. of 9 V is applied across its ends.

Electrical power

All electrical appliances change electrical energy into other forms of energy.

The meaning of power

The power of an appliance is a measure of how quickly these **energy changes take place**. This **power rating** is **measured in watts**.

A radio changes electrical energy into sound energy

If a light bulb has a **power rating of 40 W**, it **changes 40 J of electrical energy** into heat and light energy **every second**.

40W

If an electrical fire has a **power rating of 2 kW** (2000 W), **it transfers 2000 J of electrical energy** into 2000 J of heat and light energy **every second**.

How many joules of energy have been changed?

To calculate the total amount of energy an appliance has changed, we use the equation:

Energy = power × time (in seconds)

or

$$E = P \times t$$

Example

How much electrical energy is changed into heat and light energy when a 60 W bulb is turned on for five minutes?

$$\begin{aligned} E &= P \times t \\ &= 60\ W \times 300\ s \\ &= 18\ 000\ J\ or\ 18\ kJ \end{aligned}$$

Kilowatt-hours and units

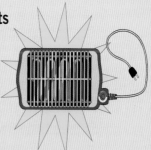

The electricity board measures the energy we use in the home in **kilowatt-hours** or units.

They calculate this value using the formula:

Energy used in kilowatt-hours
=power in kilowatts × time in hours

Example

Calculate the energy used when a 3 kW fire is turned on for two hours.

$$\begin{aligned} E &= P \times t \\ &= 3\ kW \times 2\ h \\ &= 6\ kWh\ or\ 6\ units \end{aligned}$$

The meter and the bill 1

Somewhere in your house is a **meter** like the one shown on the right. It shows how many **units of electrical energy** have been used. We usually pay our electricity bills every three months, i.e. every quarter.

The meter and the bill 2

ELECTRICITY BILL				
Charges for electricity used				
Present reading 80139	Previous reading 78579	Units used 1560	Pence per unit 11.00	Charge amount £171.60
Quarterly standing charge Total				£12.00 £183.60

By reading the meter at the beginning and end of the quarter we can calculate how many units of electrical energy have been used.

The bill shows the **number of units used** and **the cost per unit**. By multiplying these two values together we can obtain the cost of the electrical energy used.

The electricity board will also add a **standing charge** to your bill. This pays for the equipment used by the electricity board to bring the electricity into your home and for its maintenance.

Example

The readings on an electricity meter at the beginning and end of a quarter show that a family has used 800 units. The cost of one unit is 11p and the standing charge per quarter is £12.00.

Calculate the total bill for this household.

$$\text{Cost of electricity} = \frac{\text{number of units used} \times}{\text{cost per unit}}$$

$$= 800 \times 11p = £88.00$$

If the standing charge is £12.00, the total cost of the bill is:

$$£88.00 + £12.00 = £100.00$$

Calculating the power of an appliance

The power rating of an appliance can be calculated using the formula:

Power = Voltage × Current

or

$$P = V \times I$$

Example

When a voltage of 240 V is applied across a bulb, a current of 0.25 A flows. What is the power rating of this bulb?

$$P = V \times I$$
$$= 240 \times 0.25 = 60 \text{ W}$$

❶ How many joules of electrical energy are used in the following situations?

a) 100 W bulb turned on for 60 seconds
b) 500 W computer and monitor turned on for 300 seconds
c) 600 W hairdryer turned on for 2 minutes.

❷ Calculate the power of an electric fire if a current of 12.5 A flows when it is connected to a 240 V supply.

❸ How many kilowatt-hours (units) of electrical energy are converted into other forms in the following situations?

a) 3 kW fire turned on for 3 hours
b) 2 kW tumble dryer used for 30 minutes
c) 1.5 kW water heater turned on for 2 hours.

Electric motors

We use electric motors in almost every area of our lives. Whether we are listening to CDs, watching videos or DVDs, or simply lowering the electric window of a car, we are using an electric motor. When we turn a motor on, electrical energy is being used to produce motion. The descriptions below explain how this happens.

Force on a current-carrying wire

If a **current is passed through a wire** that lies **between the poles of a magnet**, there is a force on the wire. If the direction of the current or the direction of the magnetic field is changed, the direction of the force on the wire also changes.

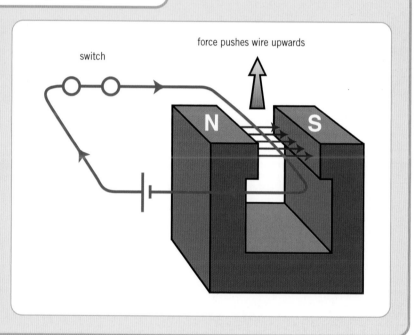

switch

force pushes wire upwards

N   S

The rotating loop of wire

- If the length of wire is replaced by a loop of wire, when current passes around it there will be a force on one side of the loop trying to push it upwards.
- There will also be a force on the opposite side of the loop trying to push it downwards.
- The effect of these two forces is to make the **loop rotate**.
- This is the basic idea behind the **electric motor**.

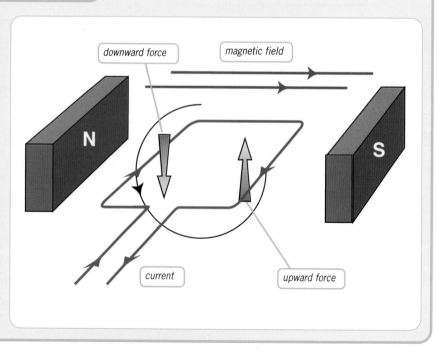

downward force

magnetic field

N   S

current   upward force

The simple electric motor

- For the loop to **rotate continuously**, the direction of the **force** on each side must **change after every half turn**, i.e. first a wire must be pushed up, then it must be pushed down.
- This change is achieved using a **split ring or commutator**.
- The split ring **changes the direction of the current** in the coil after **every half turn**.

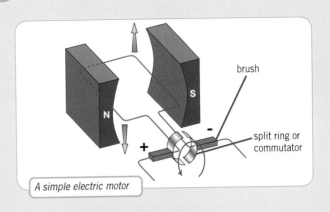

A simple electric motor

brush

split ring or commutator

To make a motor turn more quickly we can:
- increase the **current**
- increase the **number of turns on the coil**
- increase the **strength of the magnet**.

Real motors
In real, practical motors:

- the coils of wire are wrapped onto a **soft iron core** that rotates with the coil – this makes the motor **more powerful**
- **not just one but several rotating coils are used** – this makes the motor **smoother and more powerful**
- the permanent magnet is replaced with **electromagnets**.

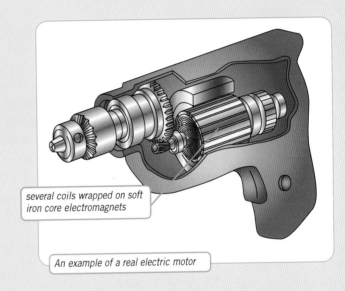

several coils wrapped on soft iron core electromagnets

An example of a real electric motor

QUICK TEST

1. What does an electric motor do?
2. Give two examples of where you will find electric motors in your home.
3. What device changes the direction of the current in an electric motor every half turn?
4. State three ways of increasing the rate of rotation of an electric motor.
5. Why are several coils used in practical motors, rather than just one?
6. A wire lying between the poles of a magnet moves upwards when current is passed through it. What will happen to the wire if each of the following is altered?

   a) the direction of the current

   b) the direction of the magnetic field

   c) the direction of the current and the magnetic field.

Generators and alternators

Currents and voltages can be made by moving wires inside a magnetic field. This process is called *electromagnetic induction*. *Generators and alternators* use this process to create the electricity we use in the home. The following shows how it works.

Electromagnetic induction

- If a wire is moved so that it crosses the field lines of a magnet, a **voltage is created across** the wire. It is called an **induced voltage**.
- If the wire is **part of a circuit**, a **current will flow**. It is called an **induced current**.
- If the **wire** is moved in the **opposite direction**, the **induced voltage and current** are in the **opposite direction**.

We can **increase the sizes** of the induced voltage/induced current by either:

- using **stronger magnets** or

- moving the wire **more quickly**.

We can also produce voltages and currents using a coil and a magnet.

- If a **magnet is moved into a coil**, a **voltage or current is induced** in the coil.
- If the **magnet is pulled out**, the induced voltage or current flows in **the opposite direction**.
- We can **increase the size** of the induced voltage or current by:

  – using a **stronger magnet**
  – **moving the magnet faster**
  – putting **more turns on the coil**.

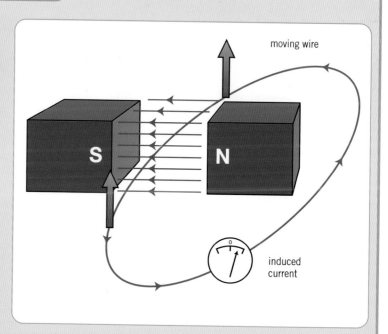

moving wire

induced current

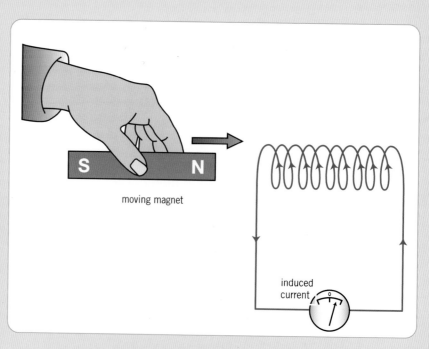

moving magnet

induced current

The simple dynamo

A **dynamo**, like the one used on a bicycle, uses these ideas to generate small currents and work the lights.

- As the wheel rotates, it causes the magnet and its **field to spin around**.
- Its magnetic field lines cut through the coil, **inducing a current** in it.
- The current that is generated keeps changing in size and direction.
- It is called an **alternating current**.

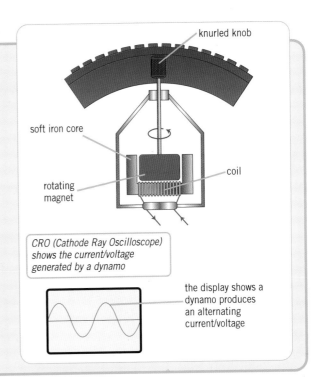

knurled knob

soft iron core

rotating magnet

coil

CRO (Cathode Ray Oscilloscope) shows the current/voltage generated by a dynamo

the display shows a dynamo produces an alternating current/voltage

Generators and alternators

- If a **coil is rotated** between the poles of a magnet, a **current is induced** in the coil.
- The wires are continually **changing direction** as they rotate and so the **induced current** also **changes in size and direction**.
- The induced current is **an alternating current**.
- A **generator that produces an alternating current** is called an **alternator**.
- The coil will generate a larger current if:
  - a **stronger magnet** is used
  - the coil is **turned more quickly**
  - a coil with **more turns** is used.

💡 *Don't let horrible phrases like 'electromagnetic induction' and 'induced current' confuse you. Just try to understand how voltages and currents can be made using magnetic fields and wires.*

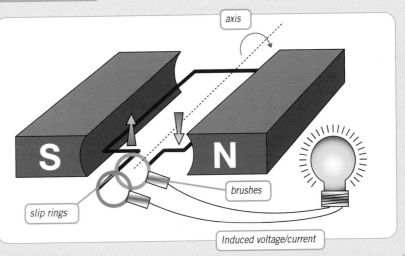

axis

S

N

slip rings

brushes

Induced voltage/current

Domestic electricity

The electricity we use in the home is known as mains electricity. It is generated at a power station and then transmitted to us through the National Grid. It differs from the electricity we use from cells and batteries in several ways.

a.c./d.c.

The electricity we get from cells and batteries is **one-way electricity**. It is called **direct current (d.c.)**.

The electricity from the mains is **continuously changing direction**. It is called **alternating current (a.c.)**.

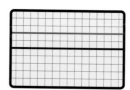

Looking at currents using a Cathode Ray Oscilloscope

A horizontal line shows a current/voltage which has a steady value and is in one direction. This is like the d.c. from a cell or battery

The electricity we get from the mains is a.c. (alternating current). 'Wave-shaped' line shows an a.c. current/voltage which is continually changing direction

The 3-pin plug

- The voltage of the electricity from cells and batteries is quite low, e.g. 9 V or 12 V.
- The voltage from the mains is about **230 V**. It **can be dangerous if not used safely**.
- **Most appliances** are therefore **connected** to the mains using **insulated plugs**.
- It is very important that the wires in a plug are connected to **the correct pins**.
- Looking at an open plug like that shown here, the **BR**own wire goes to the **B**ottom **R**ight and the **BL**ue wire goes to the **B**ottom **L**eft. The green and yellow wire (earth) goes to the pin at the top.

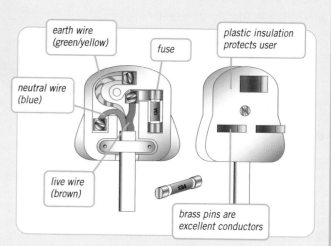

earth wire (green/yellow)

fuse

plastic insulation protects user

neutral wire (blue)

live wire (brown)

brass pins are excellent conductors

Fuses 1

All 3-pin UK plugs contain a **fuse**. This usually consists of a small **cylinder or cartridge** containing a thin piece of **wire with a low melting point**.

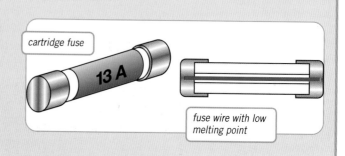

cartridge fuse

13 A

fuse wire with low melting point

Fuses 2

If a fault develops in a circuit and **too much current passes** through the fuse, the **wire melts**. The circuit becomes **incomplete** and **current ceases to pass through it**. The fuse **protects the user** and **limits any damage** to the electrical appliance.

Fuses are given a **rating** that indicates the **maximum current** that can flow through it without it melting. The most common fuses in the UK have ratings of **1 A, 3 A and 13 A**.

The correct value of a fuse is one that is **just large enough to allow the correct current to flow**, e.g. if the normal current is 2 A, a 3 A fuse is selected.

Circuit breakers
This is a **special kind of fuse** that causes a break in the circuit if too much current flows. Once the fault has been put right, the fuse is **usually reset by pushing a button**.

Residual **circuit breakers** like the one seen here are often used when mowing the lawn or using hedge trimmers. They will detect current flowing to earth if a cable is cut. The instant this happens, the supply is turned off so that the user comes to no harm.

A residual circuit breaker

The earth wire

A 3-pin plug usually has three wires connected to it.

- The **electrical energy** travels into an appliance **through the live wire**.
- The **neutral wire** is the **return path** for the current.
- The earth wire is a safety connection that **protects the user** if an appliance becomes faulty.

If a kettle has a metal casing and the heating element is broken, anyone touching the casing will receive **an electric shock**. With the **earth wire connected**, the user is safe and will not receive an electric shock.

Modern appliances such as kettles now have **plastic casings** to further reduce the risk of an electric shock for the user. The kettle has **double insulation**.

QUICK TEST

1. What kind of current is supplied through the mains?
2. Why can the mains supply be dangerous?
3. In a typical domestic plug, what colour is a) the live wire b) the earth wire and c) the neutral wire?
4. What happens to a cylinder fuse if too much current passes through it?
5. Name one advantage of a circuit breaker over a cylinder fuse.
6. Give two situations when a residual circuit breaker might be used.

Waves

Waves carry energy from place to place.
They move the energy using vibrations.
There are two main types of waves:

■ transverse waves

■ longitudinal waves.

Types of wave

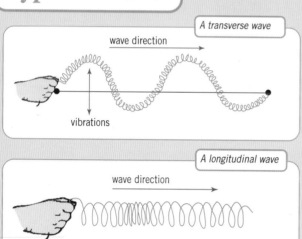

A transverse wave

wave direction

vibrations

A longitudinal wave

wave direction

vibrations

A **transverse wave** has vibrations across or at right angles to the direction in which the wave is moving. Examples of transverse waves include light waves and surface water waves.

A **longitudinal wave** has vibrations that are along the direction in which the wave is moving. Sound waves are longitudinal waves.

The important bits

- The **amplitude** of a wave is the height of a crest from the undisturbed position.
- The **wavelength** (λ) of a wave is the distance between one crest and the next.
- The **frequency** of a wave is the number of complete waves produced each second by the source. It is measured in hertz **(Hz)**.

A wave has a frequency of 200 Hz if the source is producing 200 waves each second.

The velocity of a wave (v), its frequency (f) and its wavelength (λ) are all connected by the equation:

$$v = f \times \lambda$$

Example

A sound wave has a frequency of 170 Hz and a wavelength of 2 m.

Calculate the velocity of this wave:

$$v = f \times \lambda$$
$$= 170 \times 2 = 340 \text{ m/s}$$

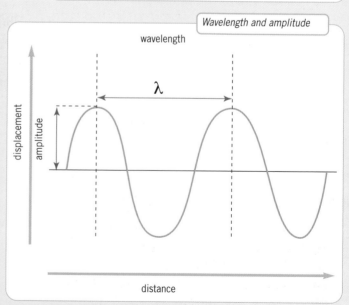

Wavelength and amplitude

wavelength

λ

displacement

amplitude

distance

Key properties of waves

When a wave strikes a plane surface, it is **reflected** so that the angle of incidence is equal to the angle of reflection.

When a waves travels across the boundary between two different mediums, its speed and direction may change, i.e. the wave is **refracted**. If the wave slows, it is refracted towards the normal. If the wave speeds up, it is refracted away from the normal. If a wave travels through a gap or across the edge of an object it may spread out. This process is called **diffraction**.

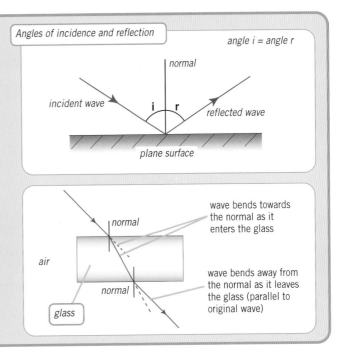

Angles of incidence and reflection

angle i = angle r

normal

incident wave

i r

reflected wave

plane surface

wave bends towards the normal as it enters the glass

normal

air

normal

wave bends away from the normal as it leaves the glass (parallel to original wave)

glass

Seismic waves

Seismic waves are **shock waves** caused by **earthquakes**. They travel through the Earth. Seismic waves can cause tremendous damage to buildings and structures on the Earth's surface. There are two types of seismic waves. They are called **P-waves** and **S-waves**.

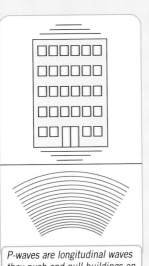

P-waves are longitudinal waves they push and pull buildings on the earths surface

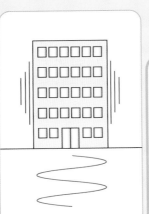

S-waves are transverse waves they shake buildings on the earths surface

Scientists have used P-waves and S-waves to learn about the **structure of the Earth**.

💡 *This is a very important topic. Understanding the basic properties of waves will help you understand the behaviour of light waves, sound waves, seismic waves, etc. Concentrate really hard on these two pages.*

Results of the shockwaves caused by an earthquake in 1994: Northridge California

QUICK TEST

1. What do waves carry from place to place?

2. Draw a wave and mark on it the wavelength and the amplitude.

3. Give one example of a transverse wave.

4. Give one example of a longitudinal wave.

5. Explain the following sentence. A guitar string produces waves with a frequency of 100 Hz.

6. A water wave has a frequency of 5 Hz and a wavelength of 3 m. Calculate the velocity of this wave.

Electromagnetic spectrum 1

This is a family of waves with a large number of common properties. They all:

- are able to travel through a vacuum
- travel at the same speed through a vacuum, i.e. the speed of light
- are transverse waves
- can be reflected
- can be absorbed
- can be transmitted
- can be refracted.

Groups within the family

Some of the **properties** of these waves **change** as their **wavelength and frequency** change.

The family is, therefore, divided into seven smaller groups.

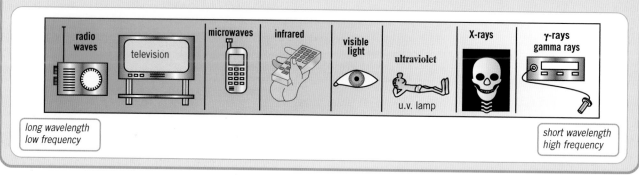

radio waves · television · microwaves · infrared · visible light · ultraviolet · u.v. lamp · X-rays · γ-rays gamma rays

long wavelength low frequency

short wavelength high frequency

Reflection, absorption and transmission

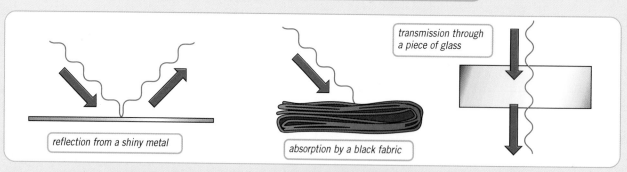

reflection from a shiny metal

absorption by a black fabric

transmission through a piece of glass

The amount of radiation (waves) that is reflected, absorbed or transmitted by an object, depends upon:

- the type of radiation being used
- the material from which the object is made
- the nature of the surface of the object, i.e. whether it is shiny or dull, etc.
- how long the object is exposed to the radiation.

If radiation is absorbed, the energy it carries may:

- warm the object
- damage living cells so that they no longer work properly, i.e. they may become cancerous
- actually kill living cells if the dose is high enough.

Biological effects of exposure to electromagnetic waves

Radio waves	No known effect
Microwaves	These are absorbed by water molecules causing body tissue to warm. Large doses can cause burns. The rapid increase in the usage of mobile phones and the erection of microwave transmitter masts close to communities is causing concern over the possible long-term effects of exposure to microwaves. At present, no one knows what the long-term effects may be.
Infrared waves	Overexposure to these waves can cause the skin to burn.
Visible light	This type of light causes chemical changes on the retina of the eye that allow us to see. Overexposure, such as looking directly at the Sun, can damage the retina and result in poor vision or even blindness.
Ultraviolet waves	These cause chemical changes in the skin resulting in tanning and premature aging. Excessive exposure will result in sunburn and possibly skin cancer. Sun blocks prevent the radiation from reaching the skin.
X-rays	These are highly penetrating rays that can cause cancer and kill living cells. Workers exposed to X-rays, such as radiographers, wear lead aprons or stand behind lead screens for protection, as X-rays cannot penetrate lead.
Gamma rays	Emitted by some radioactive materials, gamma rays are very penetrating, can cause cancer and kill living cells.

Try to remember the order of the groups of waves using the following sentence:

Reindeer	*Radio*
Meat	*Microwaves*
Is a	*Infrared*
Very	*Visible*
Unusual	*Ultraviolet*
Xmas	*X-rays*
Gift	*Gamma rays*

QUICK TEST

1. Name two properties all these waves have in common.

2. Name two features of these waves that change as we move from group to group.

3. Name three things that may happen to a living cell that absorbs some electromagnetic radiation.

4. Name two things that will determine how much radiation an object absorbs.

5. Name three groups of waves that might cause cancer.

6. Name one source of gamma waves.

Electromagnetic spectrum 2

The wavelengths of the longest waves in the spectrum are greater than many of the running events at the Olympics. The smallest have wavelengths equal to the distance between two atoms in a solid.

Radio waves

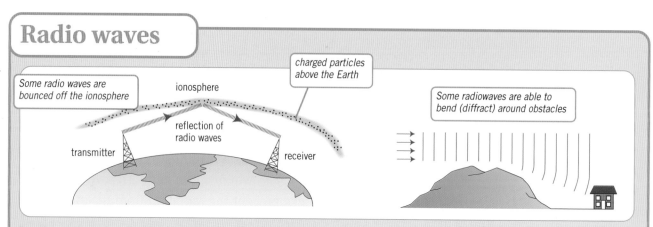

charged particles above the Earth

Some radio waves are bounced off the ionosphere

ionosphere

reflection of radio waves

transmitter

receiver

Some radiowaves are able to bend (diffract) around obstacles

Radio waves are used for **communicating over large distances**. Short wavelength radio waves are used for television broadcasting and FM radio. Longer wavelength radio waves are used for traditional AM radio.

Radio waves can carry information in two forms, **analogue** (the traditional method) and **digital** (a more modern method). Analogue signals may be distorted as they travel: digital signals are not.

Microwaves

Some microwaves pass easily through the Earth's atmosphere and so are

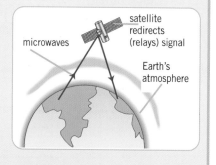

satellite redirects (relays) signal

microwaves

Earth's atmosphere

used in satellite **communication systems**, e.g. to make **international phone calls**.

Some are used for **cooking**, e.g. in **microwave ovens**. Water molecules inside the food absorb microwaves. They become 'hot', cooking the food from the inside.

food absorbs microwaves

Microwaves can be dangerous if misused. They can **cause damage to living cells**.

Infrared waves or heat radiation

All warm objects give out infrared waves. Our skin can sense or detect these waves. Overexposure causes **sunburn** but not tanning.

Infrared waves are used to **'see in the dark'**. Special **'heat seeking'** cameras create images of objects **using the infrared waves they are emitting**. These are often used by the emergency services to detect people trapped in collapsed buildings, or lost on mountains or on moors.

Remote controls for TVs and radios all use infrared waves to carry instructions.

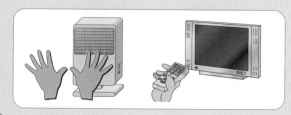

Visible light

We use these waves **to see**. It is the one part of the electromagnetic spectrum to which our **eyes are sensitive**. Visible light (and infrared light) is used to carry messages down **optical fibres**.

An optical fibre has a **high-density glass for its core** and a **less dense glass as an outer coating**. The fibre is so narrow that light entering at one end will always strike the boundary between the two glasses at a large angle. It will, therefore, undergo a series of reflections before emerging at the far end.

Optical fibres are now used to carry telephone and TV signals for cable TV.

Advantages of using optical fibres

- The fibres are cheaper than traditional copper wires.
- They are lighter.
- They can carry more signals.
- The signals they carry are more secure.

Ultraviolet

Ultraviolet waves are **emitted by the Sun**. They **cause our skins to tan**. Overexposure to ultraviolet waves can, however, **lead to skin cancer**.

When certain chemicals are exposed to ultraviolet, they **fluoresce** or

glow. Words written with security markers are only visible in ultraviolet light. Ultraviolet light can also be used to detect forged banknotes by fluorescence.

X-rays

X-rays have a very **short wavelength** and a very **high frequency**. They are **highly penetrating** and are used to look for damaged bones inside the body.

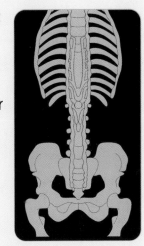

They were used to monitor the development of the foetus in the womb during pregnancy. Ultrasound is now used in preference, as it is less likely to cause any damage to the unborn baby.

Gamma rays

These are **very penetrating waves, emitted by some radioactive materials**. Gamma rays can be used to kill harmful bacteria, e.g. when sterilising surgical equipment and, if used correctly, they can also be used to kill certain kinds of cancer in the process of radiotherapy. Incorrect exposure or dosage can **damage living cells and cause cancer**.

QUICK TEST

1. Name three types of wave that can be used for communications.
2. Name two types of waves that can be used for cooking.
3. Name one type of wave that can be used to treat cancer.
4. Name two types of waves that can be sensed by human beings.
5. Give one advantage of sending signals in digital form rather than analogue.

Nuclear radiation

The nuclei of some atoms give out *radiation* all of the time. These substances are said to be *radioactive*. Three types of radiation can be emitted: *alpha*, *beta* and *gamma* radiation. All three nuclear radiations can be very useful and very dangerous. It is, therefore, important that we understand their properties.

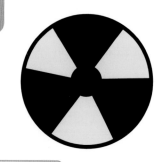

Alpha radiation (α)

Alpha particles are **slow-moving helium nuclei**, i.e. they consist of **two protons and two neutrons**. They are **big and heavy** and so have poor penetration (just a few centimetres in air). They collide with lots of atoms, **knocking some of their electrons off** and **creating ions**. They are **very good ionisers**.

An ion is an atom that has become charged by either losing or gaining electrons. Alpha particles are **positively charged** and so can be **deflected by electric and magnetic fields**.

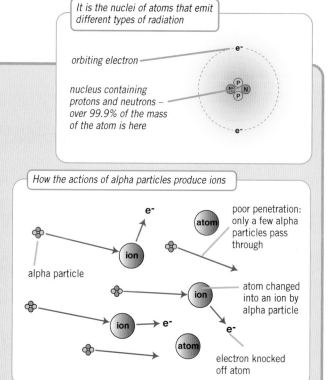

It is the nuclei of atoms that emit different types of radiation

orbiting electron

nucleus containing protons and neutrons – over 99.9% of the mass of the atom is here

How the actions of alpha particles produce ions

alpha particle

poor penetration: only a few alpha particles pass through

atom changed into an ion by alpha particle

electron knocked off atom

Beta radiation (β)

Beta particles are **fast moving electrons**. They are small and therefore have **quite good penetrating powers** (up to about a metre in air). They do collide with atoms and produce ions but not as many as the alpha particles. They are **negatively charged** and so can be **deflected by electric and magnetic fields**.

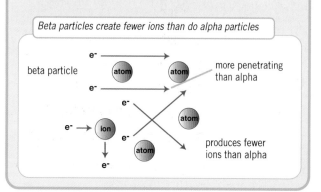

Beta particles create fewer ions than do alpha particles

beta particle

more penetrating than alpha

produces fewer ions than alpha

Gamma rays (γ)

Gamma rays are **short-wavelength electromagnetic waves**, similar to X-rays. They **travel at the speed of light** and are **very penetrating**. They can travel almost unlimited distances through air. They do not, however, hit many atoms as they travel through a material and so are **very poor ionisers**. Gamma radiation **carries no charge** and so is **unaffected by magnetic and electric fields**.

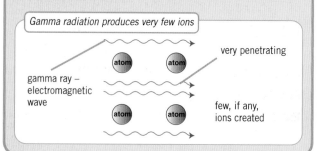

Gamma radiation produces very few ions

gamma ray – electromagnetic wave

very penetrating

few, if any, ions created

Powers of penetration

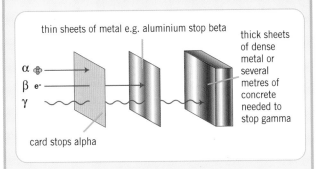

thin sheets of metal e.g. aluminium stop beta

α ⊕→
β e-→
γ ∿→

card stops alpha

thick sheets of dense metal or several metres of concrete needed to stop gamma

Exposure to radiation

Absorption of any of the three types of radiation by living cells is potentially dangerous. It may cause **cell damage** and lead to illnesses such as **cancer**. Higher levels of exposure to these radiations can **kill living cells**.

Those at most risk, such as radiographers, wear **radiation badges**. These contain photographic film that, when developed, show the **degree of exposure** to radiation experienced by that worker.

Other ways in which exposure to radiation can be reduced are by:

- wearing protective clothing
- handling radioactive materials at a distance, e.g. using tongs
- limiting the exposure time.

Exposure from sources outside the body
Alpha radiation is the least dangerous type of radiation **as it is the least penetrating and unlikely to pass through the skin**.

Beta and gamma radiations are more dangerous because they are more penetrating.

Exposure from sources inside the body
Here alpha radiation is the most dangerous type of radiation **as it is the most strongly absorbed by living cells and therefore causes most damage**. Beta and gamma radiations are

Background radiation

There are radioactive substances all around us, being used in hospitals, nuclear power stations and even in the home. Some of these substances are man-made but most are naturally occurring. They are in the ground, found in the food we eat, and even in the air we breathe. Some radiation reaches us from space. The radiation produced by these sources is called **background radiation**.

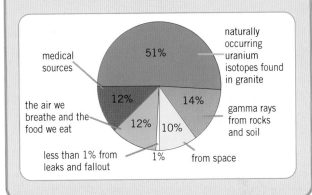

medical sources

naturally occurring uranium isotopes found in granite

51%

the air we breathe and the food we eat

12%

14%

gamma rays from rocks and soil

12%

10%

less than 1% from leaks and fallout

1%

from space

not as dangerous as they are less likely to be absorbed by living cells.

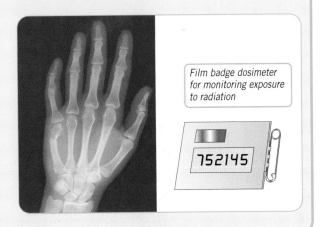

Film badge dosimeter for monitoring exposure to radiation

752145

QUICK TEST

1. Which type of radiation:
   a) is most penetrating?
   b) is the best ioniser?
   c) is negatively charged?
   d) is a fast moving electron?
   e) is an electromagnetic wave?

Uses of radioactivity

Radioactive materials are used in industry, in hospitals and even in our homes. Here are some examples.

Quality control

Sheet material such as **paper** needs to be produced to a **constant thickness**. This can be monitored using the emissions from a radioactive source.

- A **beta-emitting source** is placed above the paper.
- A beta detector is placed directly beneath it.
- If the paper becomes **thinner**, more radiation reaches the **beta detector** and the pressure between the rollers is **decreased**.
- If the paper becomes **thicker**, less radiation is detected and the pressure on the rollers is **increased**.

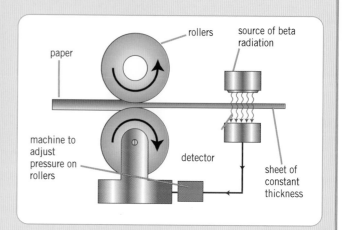

This arrangement can also be used to monitor the thickness of **sheet metal**, using a **gamma emitter** rather than a beta emitter.

Radioactive tracers

Radioactive materials can be used to **monitor the flow of liquids and gases** in pipes.

- A gamma-emitting source is added to the liquid or gas flowing through the pipe.

- This material is called a **tracer**.
- If there is a **leak** in the pipe a **higher concentration** of gamma radiation will be detected.

Using radioactive materials in this way means we do not have to dig up whole sections of roads and piping in order to find a leak.

Tracers can also be used to check the progress of fluids such as blood and digested food through the body.

For example, a radioactive material called sodium 24 can be introduced into the body to check for internal bleeding.

Radiotherapy

Some forms of cancer can be removed by surgery. Others, like brain tumours, because of their position, require a different solution. This may be **radiotherapy**.

- A **narrow beam of radiation** is directed at the **tumour** from different positions.
- A **high dose** of radiation needed to kill the cancerous cells only occurs where all the beams cross, i.e. within the tumour.

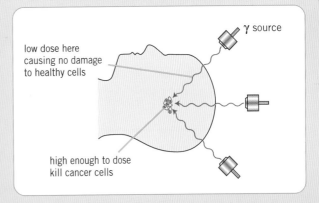

γ source

low dose here causing no damage to healthy cells

high enough to dose kill cancer cells

- In other places, the dose is not large enough to cause cell damage.

Sterilisation

Food rots because of the presence and growth of bacteria. Cooling and freezing slows down the growth of the bacteria but does not prevent it. If food is exposed to gamma radiation before being frozen, the bacteria are killed and the food keeps for much longer. This process is called **sterilisation**.

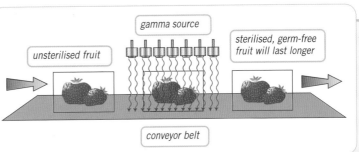

gamma source

unsterilised fruit

sterilised, germ-free fruit will last longer

conveyor belt

- Surgical instruments used to be sterilised by putting them in boiling water.
- Nowadays these instruments are sterilised by exposing them to **gamma radiation**.

Smoke detectors

Some smoke detectors like the one shown here contain a small amount of americium 241. This is an **alpha emitter**. The alpha particles create a very small current inside the detector. If smoke enters the detector this current stops or decreases. It is this change in current that triggers the alarm.

QUICK TEST

1. What kind of radiation should a source emit if it is to be used for monitoring the thickness of a) card b) sheets of steel?

2. What do we call a radioactive material we add to a liquid to monitor its flow?

3. Why should a source that emits alpha radiation not be used to check the flow of blood through the body?

4. The treatment of cancer with radiation is called ....

5. Which type of radiation is used to sterilise surgical instruments?

The Earth and our solar system

We live on a planet called Earth. It is one of many bodies that together form our solar system.

The solar system

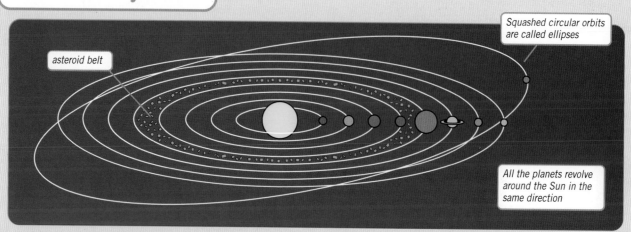

asteroid belt

Squashed circular orbits are called ellipses

All the planets revolve around the Sun in the same direction

Our solar system consists of **a star, a number of planets, moons, asteroids and comets**. We call our **star the Sun**. It contains over 99% of all the mass in our solar system. The planets, their moons, the asteroids and the comets all orbit the Sun.

The Earth is one of nine planets. In order, from the planet nearest the Sun, they are:

Mercury, Venus, Earth, Mars, Jupiter, Saturn, Uranus, Neptune and Pluto.

We can remember the order using the sentence:

Many **V**ery **E**nergetic **M**en **J**og **S**lowly **U**pto **N**ewport **P**agnell.

We see stars like the Sun because of the light they emit. **Stars are luminous** objects.

We see **planets and moons** because of the light they reflect. They are **non-luminous objects**.

Gravitational forces 1

The planets
The planets move in orbits because they **are being 'pulled' by the gravity of the Sun**. This force is called a centripetal force. Objects that are **closest to the Sun feel the strongest pull and follow the most curved paths**.

Objects that are a **long way from the Sun feel the weakest pull** and follow the **least curved orbits**.

Comets
Comets are **large rock-like pieces of ice** that orbit the Sun. They have very elliptical orbits.

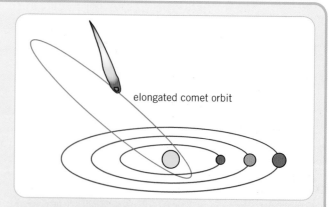

elongated comet orbit

They **travel fastest** when they are **close to the Sun** because the **gravitational forces here are large**. Close to the Sun some of a **comet's ice melts, creating a long tail**. Their velocities are lowest when they are a long way from the Sun.

Gravitational forces 2

Meteors and meteorites

Meteors are small fragments of rocks and dust that enter the Earth's atmosphere. As they fall, they become very hot and are seen as streaks of light. Very rarely, meteors reach the surface of the Earth. These space rocks are called **meteorites**. It is thought that most meteors are made up of dust and debris left behind by passing comets.

Asteroids

Asteroids are lumps of rock orbiting the Sun. They vary in size from several metres to about 1000 km in diameter. **Most asteroids** are found **in a belt** between **Mars and Jupiter** but some asteroids are found travelling outside the asteroid belt.

If a large asteroid collided with the Earth it could wipe out life as we know it. Is this likely to happen? The answer is yes. It has happened in the past, creating large craters in the Earth's surface. There is no reason to believe that it will not happen in the future, but no one knows when. Hopefully, before it happens, we will have developed the technology to prevent the collision or evacuate the Earth.

Some scientists are already suggesting that we set up a programme to look out into space and search for **Near Earth Objects**, or NEOs, which might threaten the Earth.

Satellites

Moons are **large natural satellites** that **orbit a planet**. We have just one moon, but some planets have several: for example, Mars has two, Jupiter has 16 and Saturn has 21 moons.

Artificial satellites launched by man can be put into orbit around the Earth. They have three main uses:

- To look away from Earth into deep space, e.g. the Hubble telescope.
- To monitor conditions on the surface of the Earth, e.g. weather satellites. Satellites that monitor the Earth's surface are often put into low polar orbits.
- As geostationary satellites that stay above the same place on the Earth's surface the whole time, e.g. communications satellites.

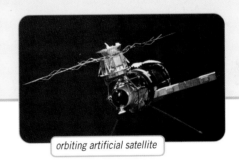
orbiting artificial satellite

Scientific process

It took a long time for scientists to develop the now accepted model of the solar system. Initially, man thought that the Earth was at the centre of the solar system. Then they believed that the Sun was at the centre and the orbits of the planets were circular. Now we believe that the Sun is at the centre, and that the planets follow elliptical orbits. Each of these changes came about because of the observations of astronomers. What they saw did not match the model. So the model had to change or be modified to match the new facts.

QUICK TEST

1. Name five different types of astronomical bodies that exist in our solar system.

2. What forces keep all the planets in orbit around the Sun?

3. What are comets made from?

4. What is an NEO and why is this a threat to the Earth?

5. What is a natural satellite?

Stars and the universe

Our Sun is a star. It is just one of billions of stars that make up the galaxy in which we live. Our galaxy is called the Milky Way. In the universe there are billions of galaxies. They are separated by distances that are often millions of times greater than the distances between stars within a galaxy.

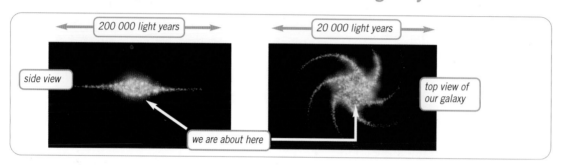

200 000 light years

20 000 light years

side view

top view of our galaxy

we are about here

How stars are born

Stars form when **particles of dust and gas** are pulled together by **gravitational forces**. These forces **compress** the particles together so tightly that there is a **very large increase in temperature**. This temperature increase sets off **nuclear reactions**. These reactions release large amounts of energy as heat and light. **Smaller amounts of gases** may form some distance away from the developing star. These may eventually **become planets and their moons**.

The origins of the universe

Our universe is **expanding**. We can see that the **most distant galaxies** are **moving away from us at the greatest speeds**. This suggests that, billions of years ago, **all the matter in the universe was in one place** and there was an explosion. This theory is called the **Big-Bang theory**.

Scientists are now asking if this expansion will continue forever, or if gravity will gradually slow it down and perhaps reverse the process, pulling all matter back to one place (**The Big Crunch**). They still do not know the answer to this question.

In most of the questions about the planets, stars and the universe, examiners are keen to see if students understand that the universe is constantly changing and that gravity plays an important role in these changes.

The life of a star

Stars change gradually with time. When a star first forms, **gravitational forces pull matter together**. When **the nuclear reactions begin**, the high temperatures create forces, which try to make the **gases expand**. When these **two forces are balanced**, the star is said to be in its **main stable period**. This period may last for billions of years. Our Sun is in this stable period.

Towards the end of the stable period a different type of nuclear reaction begins. As a result, the **star begins to expand** and becomes a little **cooler**. The star is changing into a **red giant**. Some time later, a different kind of nuclear reaction begins. On this occasion the expansive forces are less than the **forces of gravity** and so the star becomes much smaller. It is now changing into a **white dwarf**. As a white dwarf **cools**, it **changes** to become a **cold black dwarf star**.

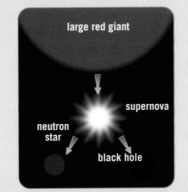

Stars much larger than our Sun may have a slightly different future. They first change into a very large red giant called a super red giant. When the star eventually cools, it shrinks and becomes unstable. An explosion then follows, throwing dust and gas into space. An **exploding star** like this is called a **supernova**.

Any matter that is left behind after the explosion may form a **very dense neutron star** or **black hole**. The gravity of a black hole is so strong that even **light is unable to escape**.

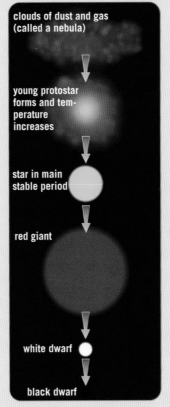

clouds of dust and gas (called a nebula)

young protostar forms and temperature increases

star in main stable period

red giant

white dwarf

black dwarf

---

❶ What is the name of our nearest star?

❷ What is the name of the galaxy in which we live?

❸ What forces bring together particles of dust and gas to form a star?

❹ What kinds of reactions cause the temperature of a forming star to increase?

❺ How was matter in the universe distributed in the beginning, according to the Big-Bang theory?

Exploring space

Apart from the Earth and the Moon, humans have not visited any of the other bodies in the universe. Nevertheless, we have lots of information about them. Much of this has come from observations made by telescope and data collected by probes.

Telescopes

Before the invention of telescopes, all human observations were made with the **unaided eye**. Consequently, our view of the universe was very limited. **Optical telescopes** greatly increased our abilities to see and identify new astronomical bodies in our solar system, e.g. the moons of Jupiter and the outermost planets. Large optical telescopes, can see even further into space. They are often built on mountaintops – where the images we see suffer fewer **distortions** from the **Earth's atmosphere** than those at sea level.

Another way to avoid these distortions is to mount **telescopes on satellites**, which orbit the Earth high above its atmosphere. A good example of this is the **Hubble telescope**, which was launched in 1990. It has seen **further into space** than any previous telescope.

Some modern telescopes use **other parts of the electromagnetic spectrum** to gather data. These include **radio waves, infrared and ultraviolet radiation**.

Probes

Flybys are unmanned probes that fly **close to, or are put in orbit** around, a planet or a moon in order to **gather information**, which is then sent back to Earth.

Landers are unmanned probes that actually **land on the surface of a moon or planet**. They often carry out simple experiments, e.g. **testing soil samples, analysing the planet's or moon's atmosphere, gravitational or magnetic field, etc**. They can provide more detailed information than the flyby probes but are **far more expensive**.

Manned missions 1

We could gather even more detailed information about other planets and moons by sending out manned probes, but the **extra cost is enormous**. Most of this increase is due to the extra consideration that has to be given to **providing astronauts with an environment** which will keep them safe for the duration of the trip.

- There is **no air or oxygen in space** so this must be taken with them. There is the possibility in the future that, for longer journeys, plants could be grown on board a spacecraft to provide some of the oxygen necessary.

Manned missions 2

- Sufficient **water and food** must also be taken along. There is the hope that in the future perhaps some of this water may be found elsewhere in space, e.g. from comets.
- There must be sufficient **fuel on board for the outward and the return journey**. There is no need for the return journey with an unmanned probe.
- The Earth's atmosphere protects us from cosmic radiation, micrometeorites and much of the Sun's ultraviolet radiation. In space, this will not be the case so **radiation shields** will need to be included in the spacecraft's design.
- Gravity during a journey in space will be much less than that on Earth. In fact, for most of the time astronauts will experience **weightlessness**. This can have serious long-term effects on their health. Because astronauts have to do far less work against gravity, this is likely to lead to: a) **calcium depletion**, which may cause bones to become brittle and b) **muscle wastage**. The effects of both of these problems may be overcome by astronauts **exercising daily** during the journey or providing them with '**artificial gravity**'.
- Temperatures in space can vary enormously from −270°C to in excess of 200°C. A very narrow temperature range (approx 10°C to 30°C) needs to be maintained for manned flights. Maintaining this range will require energy, i.e. for cooling or heating.

The benefits of exploring space

Exploring space is very costly but there have been many spin-offs and benefits. These include:

- smoke detectors
- weather and communications satellites
- space blankets
- flat panel TVs
- high-power batteries for cordless tools
- PTFE (non-stick pans)
- mobile phones
- ultrasound scanners
- in-car navigation systems
- air traffic control collision avoidance systems.

Mars Observer which was sent to Mars in 1992

QUICK TEST

1. Why are some telescopes built on top of mountains?
2. Explain the difference between a flyby probe and a lander. Give one example of each.
3. Give four reasons why manned flights are much more expensive than unmanned flights.
4. Give four spin-offs or benefits there have been from the exploration of space.

Practice questions

Use the questions to test your progress. Check your answers on page 126.

1. What kind of energy is electrical energy transferred into by a: a) speaker ....
   b) bulb .... c) hairdryer .... d) battery charger ....

2. 100 J of electrical energy enter a light bulb. Just 10 J of this energy is changed into light energy. What is the efficiency of the bulb? What happens to the other 90 J of electrical energy?
   ....

3. Explain what is meant by the phrase 'renewable source of energy'. Name three renewable sources of energy.
   ....

4. The diagram shows a hydroelectric power station.
   a) What kind of energy does the water possess in the top lake?
      ....
   b) What kind of energy does the water possess as it enters the turbine?
      ....
   c) Explain how surplus energy could be stored until it is needed.
      ....

5. Explain why double glazing is a better form of insulation than a single pane of thick glass.
   ....

6. Explain how cavity wall insulation reduces heat loss from a house.
   ....

7. Name five different ways in which you could insulate your house so that it loses less energy.
   ....

8. Give one use for a variable resistor.
   ....

9. Explain the difference between a thermistor and an LDR.
   ....

10. A current of 2 A flows when a p.d. of 12 V is applied across a wire. Calculate the resistance of the wire.
    ....

11. A fire has a power rating of 500 W. Explain what this means.
    ....

12. When a voltage of 240 V is applied across a bulb, a current of 0.5 A flows. What is the power rating of this bulb?
    ....

13. Name three ways in which we could make a motor go faster.
    ....